AUDIE MURPHY IN SAIGON

This is a work of fiction & nonfiction.

LIBRARY OF CONGRESS IN PUBLICATION DATA
ISBN: 978-0-578-22683-5
Category: Literature/Criticism/Vietnam War/Fiction/Nonfiction
Written by Edgar Tiffany
Book Cover Art Credit to Kenneth Keys, Bakersfield, CA.
Cover & Text Layout by
Eli Blyden | www.EliTheBookGuy.com
Printed in the United States of America by
A&A Printing & Publishing | www.PrintShopCentral.com

ACKNOWLEDGMENTS

"The King Teaches His Educated Son a Lesson," was first published as "Memento Mori" in *ZEITGEIST* ©1978, Old Dominion University, Vol. 1, No. 2; "The Triple-Canopied Jungle," ©1985, *American Book Review;* "War and Remembrance," ©1995, *STYLE WEEKLY;* "Saigon Passional" ©2006, *Veterans of War, Veterans of Peace* (Edited by Maxine Hong Kingston).

In Memoriam, Merton Miles Tiffany,
March 6, 1948 - August 20, 1998
Son, Brother, Father, Husband,
Soldier, Aviator and Hero

AUDIE MURPHY IN SAIGON

無

– Japanese Kanji for "Nothingness"

AUDIE MURPHY IN SAIGON

TABLE OF CONTENTS

Foreword

I first encountered Edgar Tiffany ("Hiya, buddy, my name's Buzz. I got the fuzz. I make the elevator do what she does.")[1] in the Richmond Downtown YMCA weight room. In the early nineties I was in my thirties, and Buzz in his fifties. That did not prevent him from toiling under an Olympic Bar rattling with eight forty-five-pound plates. I cannot remember how our conversation began, but it might have occurred spotting each other at the incline bench. I do recall some classical allusions being fired like an artillery round is "fired for effect." That back and forth, recalling literature, art, music, continues to this day as a means of both defining, and expanding the depth and breadth of my understanding of this complex writer.

[1] Buzz, the elevator operator, is a character in *The Hudsucker Proxy*, a film which came out in 1994, about the time I met Edgar "Buzz" Tiffany. The role was played by Jim True, more famous later for playing Roland "Prez" Prysbylewski on five seasons of *The Wire*. When Buzz met anyone new, he introduced himself with this line. If someone queried him, "What are you talkin about?" he explained carefully, "It's a line from the *Hudsucker Proxy*. See it. Paul Newman's in it."

That's not to say we are, or were, highfalutin. Buzz loves the profane, and the just plain idiotic as much as the oracular, perhaps, like me, but even more so. For example the reference to Audie Murphy in Saigon, for those of us who haven't followed Audie's film career perhaps as closely as we should have, connects the real life Medal of Honor awardee and most decorated soldier in World War II with the Graham Green novel *The Quiet American,* and the American propaganda film in which he starred in 1957, while put up in the downtown version of Saigon's Ritz-Paris. And it makes an ironical, but sly reference to the very kind of war conducted over time in Vietnam and the contradiction of it in the name of Murphy. Saigon stood for the war of generals, diplomats, civil servants and logistical savants. Audie Murphy stood for the essence of the war-fighter. Audie Murphy in Saigon is like saying Audie Murphy in Washington DC. Or for the purpose of time reality in 1943-1945, "Audie Murphy in London."

But the largest irony is the film itself. American director Joseph Mankiewicz rewrote Greene's novel for the screen, managing to turn what was a nuanced, prescient warning to America and the world about Vietnam into a potboiler, love-triangle story. This motif of whitewashing the Vietnam experience in literature and film for the sake of "art," political expediency, and just plain old greed, has been a recurring theme in writing about Vietnam ever since and "Anti-Memoirs" and *Audie Murphy in Vietnam*, evoking the honor and valor of Audie Murphy in juxtaposition, takes a microscope to it. Tiffany, having been "in country" from 1966-1967 and several times after the U.S. embargo was lifted in 1994, has had a front row seat to the whole of it. He is more than a run of the mill spectator. He was a combatant who has both killed men, and attempted to save them, all while receiving his own injuries in the process. He is quick to point out authors and directors whose information is often second hand, and third rate. If that ruffles the feathers of the critically acclaimed so much the better, since both the living and the dead deserve the truth. If it is *beau sabreur* John Wayne stories you are looking for you are barking up the wrong tree. The heroism mentioned in these pages is factual and meticulously footnoted from a myriad of original sources.

It is significant that Tiffany begins with a tale not of the kind of heroism Audie Murphy became known for in "To Hell and Back," but with a report of a nocturnal ambush gone horribly wrong. Told from the point of view of "H.," Tiffany relates the effects of a claymore mine mistakenly detonated by an ambush on a group of women and children traversing a path in order to get an early start for a stall at a crowded market place. Trained as a medic, he provides what aid he can, and recalls a young boy holding his grandmother's head in his lap as she lay shot through with the mine's ball-bearing payload. What he recalls is a look of anger, and hatred, that can never be unseen. Perhaps that image encapsulates both the American, and Vietnamese, experience of the war better than the several hours of "Apocalypse Now," a film he once described to me as "a civilian's wet dream."

What you will find in the pages that follow is a writer who has read, and watched widely, over the past forty years most of what has been written and thought about his war. He draws on everyone from Virgil, and Homer to Joyce, and even the crackpot fake green beret Michael Cimino who struts and frets his minute upon the lot stage. The impression a reader is left with is that of a man driven to Ahabesque extremes to make sense of the senseless, deal truth to the false, lampoon all that is fake in war and religion, and bring down the mighty with some damn funny parodies, granular short stories, and historical "what ifs."

Oh. And by the way, poetry being my first love, it is evident from his prose that Tiffany could have been a poet, for like most writers of any kind, he went through a fascination with the form, like a love of certain music. The brief appearance of his verse in this volume will tell you that. My first connection with Tiffany resulted in mention of him in a poem I wrote in the 90's entitled *The Moorish Cantos*:

I.

America. Thanks
for the M-1 tanks.
Please know
It is not compassion
stalks the sand
that blows
up our racing camel's nose.

II.

You say you are my husband.
You are a Viking of the seventh order.
Try to leave our abode without sulking,
or you'll have a one-woman jihad.

III.

May the wife of the deposed Shah
ignite Rafsanjani's heart
and incite him to broadcast
Saturday Night Fever
into the televisions
of Iran's most faithful.

IV.

For she has read the Shahnameh of
Abul-Qâsem Ferdowsi Tusi ابوالقاسم فردوسی طوسی,
or just Ferdowsi فردوسی—
Khwāja Shams-ud-Dīn Muḥammad Ḥāfeẓ-e Shīrāzī
(خواجه شمس‌الدین محمد حافظ شیرازی),
known by his pen name Hafez حافظ '
the memorizer; the (safe) keeper',
Who lauded the joys of love and wine,
but would jihad a religious nut.
And now found the delights of E. Buzz Tiffany in
the rudimentary fact he showed her
there will be an afterlife,
in the grave.
وما إلى ذلك وهلم جرا
wama 'iilaa dhlk wahalam jirana

And here is what I referred to. He said he wrote this many years ago after a nightmare about a snake that tempted him in the jungle around the Parrots' Beak (not the bird's bill, but in 1966, a nightmare of geography on the South Vietnam/ Cambodian border). A poem entitled the "Undiscovered Country" appears as some kind of *nonjaculus* nightmare, and it is, but to look closely is to reveal that it is hammered to the scaffolding of Wilfred Owen's *Dulce et Decorum Est,* line for line, verse for verse, quirk for quirk:

A dark, unsightly bubol, red and deep,
Exuding scents of what? What's on the skin
Of that white-linened whore from Tu Do Street
That's ripe and pungent as a durian,
Surprising as the stink of camembert?
Two coal-tarred scars are carved around her knees
To staunch the sap from dribbling to the dirt
Amid the quincunx aisles of rubber trees.

Three soldiers sit upon packed ammo crates
Eating Baked Dog DiRocco from a steel
(Clean the glands from 'neath the skinned dog's legs,
Or bitterness will sabotage the meal);
Fry bacon, 10 bay leaves, ground peppercorn
And season with nuoc mam and juice of lime.

This is the way our own deaths were forsworn–
Au poivre and buried in a pit of lime.

I find myself naked on a table
Where an embalmer runs a silver tube
Into my groin and begins to ladle
From a pot of dark and simmering soup.
But faintly on the tin roof of this morgue–
Tapping like the search of feeding woodcocks
Or, a rap upon a door
From rigid fingers hushed in woolen socks–
A noise that wakes me from this worried sleep.
Relieved, I see the darkness of my room,
Its six squared walls erected six feet deep–
Was just my restless hands tracing my tomb.

Is this iambic pentameter? Yes it is and, No it isn't. Since it is a mirror image of *"Dulce et Decorum Est"* except for the words, it bucks the iambic pentameter trend. In iambic pentameter, every line should follow an unstressed/stressed syllable pattern. Shakespeare's sonnets are written in a rhyme scheme in which each sonnet line consists of ten syllables. An iamb is one unstressed syllable followed by one stressed. kaBOOM/ kaBOOM/kaBOOM/kaBOOM/kaBOOM.

*Shall **I** comPARE thee TO a SUMmer's DAY?*
Thous ART more LOVEly AND more TEMperATE

(Sonnet 18)

"*Dulce et Decorum Est*," doesn't follow this pattern. It starts this way, then bursts that form like the artillery barrage Owen led his platoon through near the town of St. Quentin on April Fools Day, 1917, as apt a day to discover in the sacrifice of such a mission, that the enemy had already withdrawn from their trenches. This very barrage was, no doubt, the catalyst for *Dulce et Decorum Est*.

Bent double, like old beggars under sacks,
Knock-kneed, coughing like hags, we cursed through sludge,
Till on the haunting flares we turned our backs,
And towards our distant rest began to trudge.
Men marched asleep. Many had lost their boots,
But limped on, blood-shod. All went lame; all blind;
Drunk with fatigue; deaf even to the hoots
Of gas-shells dropping softly behind.

Now compare that first stanza to Tiffany's:

A dark, unsightly bubol, red and deep,
Exuding scents of what? What's on the skin Of
that white-linened whore from Tu Do Street
That's ripe and pungent as a durian,
Surprising as the stink of camembert?
Two coal-tarred scars are carved around her knees

To staunch the sap from dribbling to the dirt
Amid the quincunx aisles of rubber trees.

Of a helicopter assault into a hot landing zone in Tay Ninh Province near the Cambodian border, Tiffany wrote "I remember watching the orange-plumed clusters of high explosive walking in measured step through the towering canopy; ordnance shot from heavy guns poised round a church steeple in far off Dau Tieng." And later, "Michael Herr's prose and his dictions are the heavy artillery recalling Vietnam for all of us, one way or another." Included in this volume, Tiffany wrote this in a book review of Michael Herr's *Dispatches* marking the Tenth anniversary of the U.S. exit from Vietnam. Like Owen, Tiffany knew the heavy dictions of artillery.

Is this version of *Dulce et Decorum Est* famous? Is it even published? No. But it should have been included in *Audie Murphy in Saigon*, and now it is. After reading the closing "discovered manuscript" of "The Roman," I believe that Tiffany may well be the most war-experienced, Christ-obsessed, autodidact, and atheist writer of the last several decades. He is more akin to Pound than a prose writer, and more poetic that the best of the Cantos. He is another

American writer "gone native" in a foreign country never to fully return, and it is for that we should salute him.

James Huneycutt
Richmond, Virginia

AUDIE MURPHY IN SAIGON

FICTIONS AND NONFICTIONS

by EDGAR TIFFANY

Part One
NONFICTIONS

AUDIE MURPHY IN SAIGON

VIETNAM ANTI-MEMOIRS

Forsan et haec olim
meminisse juvabit.[2]

– Virgil, *Aeneid*, Book I

After a time even the most tragic name
acquires a kind of beauty.

– Paul Scott, *The Jewel in the Crown*

---

2 Aeneas tells his exhausted shipwrecked crew, "Perhaps this too will be a pleasure to look back on one day."

I – The Dark Side Of The Moon

H. wrote an After Action Report of an ambush gone wrong near a village in the Republic of Vietnam named Phu Cuong. On October 26, 1966, H. was a combat medic assigned to Company A, 2nd Bn, 16th Infantry Rangers, First Infantry Division. H. was the medic for a rifle platoon designated MIKE which, along with the other elements of Company A, was conducting search and seal missions and night ambushes on the Saigon River and environs in Lai Thieu District about 15 kilometers due north of Tan Son Knut Air Base. These small-unit tactical forays were carried out under First Division Command in Operation Allentown South, in a District Government of Vietnam (GVN) Outpost and Armory located in the town of Lai Thieu at map coordinates XT861059 and not far from a spot on the map named Phu Cuong.[3] GVN District forces were attached and integrated into all 2/16th platoons and squads during these search and seal and ambush missions. [4] The ambush operations

---

[3] Daily Sitrep for 2/16th Infantry, 26 October 1966.
[4] Daily Staff Journal or Duty Officer's Log, 2/16th Infantry, 22 October 1966, p. 2.

involved squad and two squad units of American and GVN forces moving to ambush sites by walking, riding in motor vehicles or landing from river assault group (RAG) boats.[5]

A permanent curfew had been in effect for several months in this area (all of the local population were required to remain in their homes after dusk and before sunrise) but had not often been enforced by the GVN or other allied units which obeyed an implied rule of engagement: "If it moves after 1900 hours and before 0600 hours, shoot it." Under these conditions nine ambush elements departed Lai Thieu District Command Post at about 1815 hours October 26th by two and a-half ton trucks dispersing at nine ambush sites located in a 30 square kilometer area north of Lai Thieu and south to Phu Cuong.[6]

H. was attached to ambush A-7 which was to locate at map coordinates XT835106. This ambush element was two squads strong consisting of nine Americans and eight GVN with a GVN interpreter translating from Vietnamese to English.[7] The site of the A-7 ambush was about 500 meters south of

---

[5] *Ibid.*

[6] Daily Sitrep for 2/16th Infantry, 27 October 1966, p. 1. (see footnote 7)

[7] Daily Sitrep for 2/16th Infantry, 26 October 1966.

QL 13, a paved national highway and 200 meters from an all-weather, light-surface, one-lane road bisecting QL 13 that led southwest for four kilometers before shrinking to a footpath.

The physical geography of Lai Thieu District was notable for a crescent of rice paddies surrounding a heavily populated delta of five or six square kilometers. This area resembled the delta country located south of Saigon described by William Prochnau in his volume on the early Vietnam War, *Once Upon a Distant War*:

"The tree lines grew like typhoon windbreaks in the flat, exposed expanse of the river's plain. A mix of banana trees, coconut palms, thick bamboo, and assorted tropical hardwoods made sightings from the air all but impossible and a barricade of lush, verdant undergrowth reduced ground-level visibility to a matter of feet—or inches. A lattice of canals and creeks, their banks often so overgrown they could hide scouts and runners, provided passageways to and from the thickets."[8]

---

[8] William Prochnau, *Once Upon a Distant War*, (New York: Vintage Books, 1995) p. 218.

Near the A-7 ambush site was a minor pagoda and a cemetery. The ambush was set about 50 meters from a trail leading from south to north, one of many footpaths and cart trails which criss-crossed the area connecting the random houses of the many small villages in the district.[9]

The passage of the night for A-7 was uneventful from the moment the ambush patrol crawled a final 200 meters into position from northwest of the cemetery (shown on Map #2 at XT837107) until 0400 hours the next morning. Ambushes were normally uneventful with the ambushing unit spending about ten hours immobile in one spot observing in silence a trail or site of opportunity. However, at about 0420

---

[9] Map #1 is from SAIGON *1:50,000, Sheet 6330 IV, Series L7014*, showing the area of Lai Thieu District with site of ambush marked at XT835106. Map #2 is the area of detail. UTM grid coordinates are derived by reading across the top of the map to a numbered grid or block which is divided into tenths from 1 to 9 (for instance, a reading of 835 means grid square 83.5, or one-half the distance into the square) and vertically on the map to 10 moving within the grid square the necessary part of a decimal of 10 (in this case, 104). Each grid square represents a square kilometer (the distance between the town of Phu Cuong and Lai Thieu on Map #1 is approximately 9 grid squares or 9 kilometers).

hours on the morning of October 27th, ambush element A-6 which was positioned two kilometers due south of A-7 at Ap Binh Phu off a single lane, light-surface road reported by radio that it had "observed 25 women and children carrying torches and baskets as if going to market."[10] In the after-action debriefing A-7 revealed that it had not heard this radio transmission.

This was the first of two tragic lapses for the women and children walking to market place in violation of the curfew. After action evidence determined that this group was taking the product of its gardens and other items six or seven kilometers to Phu Cuong open-air market and was willing to break the martial-imposed curfew to find an advantageous selling booth—this in response to the lax enforcement of that curfew in the past.

The column of women and children carrying this produce proceeded due north from the A-6 ambush at Ap Binh Phu (XT837084) following a footpath (marked intermittently on the map) for about two kilometers where they crossed the one lane, light-surface road 500 meters south of QL 13.

---

[10] Daily Staff Journal or Duty Officer's Log, 27 October 1966, p. 1. (See also Map #2)

They then skirted, unwittingly, by about 200 meters southward the A-8 ambush set up on the single lane road to the east of the pagoda (at XT836104) and continued northwest the short 400 meters to the minor pagoda and cemetery where (A-7) waited in ambush 20 meters off the trail they were now walking on.[11]

H. had spent the ensuing hours in a flank element of the triangular ambush facing away from the trail along which the women and children would approach. Each point of the triangle ambush contained six men, one point covering the trail, the other two points covering the remaining 240 degrees of the compass. From each point one or more M18A1 claymore mines were strung out giving the patrol 360 degrees of discreet coverage from a directional device with 700 steel balls set in an explosive bed and electrically fired by an observer operated switch. The claymore is a devastating anti-personnel mine and because it is separated from the observer/detonator by up to 30 meters, also provides the kind of misdirection needed in ambush; the site of the explosion is not the site of the personnel triggering it. Upon detonation,

[11] See Map #2, Grid Square XT835106.

the claymore propels the steel balls outward in a 60-degree fan-shaped swathe which is lethal up to 50 meters.[12]

During the night the point members traded off hours of watch and sleep. H. was awakened at around 0500 hours, October 27th' by the explosion of an M18 claymore mine. H. had been sleeping since 0330 hours after pulling change watch. While the Daily Staff Journal reports that A-7 fired on the suspected Viet-Cong, the only action initiated against the file of women and children was the detonation of the claymore.[13] The sequence of response, if the ambush was fired on after detonation of the claymore, would have been grenades then gunfire. No fire was received from the ambushed column as they had none to give.

By the time the file of women and children had approached A-7 at XT835106, they had extinguished the torches they were seen carrying an hour earlier at A-6's site. Perhaps they did this because dawn was arriving or they had heard noises from A-6 and A-8 lying in

---

[12] Arthur Robinson, ed., *Weapons of the Vietnam War*, (Greenwich: Bison Book Corps., 1983) p. 33.
[13] Daily Staff Journal or Duty Officer's Log, 27 October 1966, p. 1.

wait further back in their journey, or both. The Vietnamese GVN interpreter with the point element of A-7 told the A-7 patrol leader that Viet Cong were intermingled with the women and children going to market place and were using them, as was often reputed, as cover during passage through Phu Cuong. This was the second tragic miscue. Combined with the noise of women bearing baskets and other containers snapping upon the springing balance of carrying poles and the absence of torchlight, the A-7 patrol leader triggered a single claymore mine at about 0500 hours.[14]

What H. heard with the rest of the patrol from 0500 hours until 0600 hours, when dawn finally arrived, were the cries and whispers of wounded women and children fallen no more than 30 meters away. Because security and close support protocols had to be followed the patrol could not move to the wounded until first light and then only after the Battalion had begun moving other combat teams into the area to cover what at that moment was an unsure and potentially volatile situation.

---

14 *Ibid.*

First light revealed that the trail, for 25 to 30 meters, was littered with fallen women and children. H. moved to inspect the kinds of wounds the column had suffered. Because steel balls had mowed across the trail at no more than two to three feet high many of the women had suffered traumatic amputations of the legs. The children who numbered about four, where horribly wounded because the swathe of pellets had hit them squarely in the belly and chest areas. H. remembered being surprised on first examination, considering the immensity of the wounds, how little bleeding there was. H. remembered that he thought the proof of the complete destructive force of the claymore was verified when he saw sprawled at the very front of this column the mutilated remains of a dog which had been leading and, standing two to three feet high, had taken the full impact of the claymore's arc.

H. was the only medic in the area. His medical aid bag was stocked with very few items necessary to treat the immensity of the wounds on that trail that morning. H. had two or three rolled wire ladder splints and cravats. H. collected battlefield dressing carried by all patrol members. Using the wire ladder splints, cravats and battlefield dressings he bound into place legs that were left hanging and importuned for anything that could be used as a splint to hold in place the torn and severed limbs of the victims. H. also exhausted immediately the morphine syrettes he carried as a controlled amount. H. had one canned albumin unit which he attempted to administer to one of the wounded going into shock, but could not find a vessel large enough to take the needle. Within minutes a helicopter landed out of range of the patrol bringing in First Division command personnel. GVN forces began arriving in trucks and a non-military ambulance arrived. Vietnamese medical personnel entered the patrol area and 2/16th and GVN forces began cordoning the area off from the Vietnamese who were peers, friends and perhaps family of these women and children now lying on this trail. H. recalled, vividly, that none of these peasant women were evacuated by helicopter. They were carried on litters from the pathway and loaded into the ambulance that had backed down the ambush trail. Except for after action interviews of all the patrol members for details of the night's events no further mention was made of the ambush, no disciplinary actions arose out of it and, except for the intermittent resurrection by patrol members over the coming months, the details and events of that night merged into the many combat actions the 2/16th Infantry would be involved in over the next several months.[15]

The Daily Staff Journal recorded that seven of the market group died, one enroute to the hospital and six were wounded. [16] H. remembered clearly, however, that every one of the 25 members of that entourage, from the dog in front to the woman bringing up the rear, had received some kind of wound from the wide swathe cut by the exploding claymore.

H. didn't get the unit records (After-Action Reports, Daily Journals, Situation Reports) until 20 years after he wrote a recalled impression of the ambush at Phu Cuong for a writing class in college in 1973. While memory has been proven to be a faulty reporter of the facts, Army records in 1966 are more notable for what they didn't say, than what they did. H.'s 1973 account was written in the heat of memory six short years later recalling these non-historical facts.

---

[15] 2/16th Infantry would fight in two of the largest ground operations conducted in the Vietnam War in the next four months; Operations Attleboro and Junction City.

[16] Daily Staff Journal or Duty Officer's Log, 27 October 1966, p. 2.

"The squad had moved in on itself as the light brought sun and security. The men began to move stealthily toward the shattered path, the path where they knew death waited. As he broke through the foliage, he saw a small dog lying, cross-legged and gutted, upon the trail. To his left the myriad of colors wrenched his attention and the focus jolted him. Women. Children. There, stretched for fifty meters rested the sprawled wreckage of peasant women, and their children, their produce baskets on wicker sticks shattered, staining them, being stained by them.

He began looking for life and found it in a child with no legs and found it again in an old woman with punctured limbs. He used his morphine without thought, used it to replace the moaning words they used for comfort. He found a limb and placed in on the person nearest to it, tied it fast with wire splint and cravats. The women who lived, looked with huge eyes at these tree-colored men roaming up and down the trail with black guns in their hands. They cowered in their pain, seeming to await further brutality. They were even sheepish in their agony. As he toiled over the wounds he repeated again and again, 'I'm sorry, I'm sorry.' They shrunk from his words.

The helicopters began to circle round the group of soldiers. With the helicopters and dawn had come the villagers—the fathers, the brothers, the mothers, the sons, daughter, sisters of these mangled women and children. They moved slowly down the trail viewing the soldiers milling about their fallen kin and began to moan in anguish. Some came hesitantly to cradle the body of one dear to them. Others quivered near the clearing, afraid that this too would be their fate.

The dead and wounded were being moved by litters to ARVN[17] ambulance trucks. The Sector officer, a fat Vietnamese in charge of a garrison of ARVN soldiers somewhere in the hamlet, was talking with the American commander standing away from the tragedy. He was standing beside the broken body of an old woman. A boy of twelve or thirteen cradled her head in his lap, rocking her, soothing her with his tears and singing voice. He looked down, the boy's grief transfixing him. He reached for his shoulder.

'I'm sorry, I'm sorry.'

---

[17] Abbreviation for the regular forces of the Army of the Republic of South Vietnam.

The boy recoiled violently, his eyes dark with rage. He drew back. The hate in the boy's eyes shocked him, stripped him. He turned away quickly, feeling for all the world that he had pulled the trigger on the claymore.

As the last of the living and the dead were removed and the villagers had turned away, he saw the Vietnamese Sector officer and the American moving toward a helicopter standing at the edge of the clearing. They were smiling and the Vietnamese seemed to be continuously touching the American commander with his fingers."

II – Between The Idea And The Reality

H. left Phu Cuong and other memorable landmarks in 1967, and sought his therapy in looking for Vietnam ever after in literary terms, or in the literature. From the time H. came back, but stayed in uniform for several more years, he was always looking out for someone's novel about Vietnam, or some viewpoint that would capture some essence of the war-period Vietnam; one, ironically, that wasn't about combat, or necessarily about the American experience (read *Yellow Fever*, by Jean Larteguy (France), *Into a Black Sun* by Takisha Kaiko (Japan), *Saigon* by Anthony Grey (U.K.), *Best We Forget* by Bernard Clancy (Australia); and to get really obscure, *The Brinkman*, by Desmond Meiring (Kenya, Africa), and most recently, *The Sympathizer*, by Viet Thanh Nguyen (Vietnam via the University of California, Berkeley)); or to tell the truth, looking for an American Conrad, or Greene—but someone once said that all the Conrads and Greenes (and Dostoevskys and Tolstoys) of America were attending Princeton, Yale, Harvard in the 50's, 60's, and 70's with draft deferments. A New York poet and writer,

Barry Wallenstein, hit the nail on the head a long time ago:

"Such a war [Vietnam] and its ramifications cry out for a strong literary response, a literature of grim probing, reminiscent of Sartre's wall, Melville's whiteness, Dostoevsky's underground, or Conrad's most adaptable dark interior. All these attempts to get the truth straight, factually, psychologically and morally."[18]

Oddly, you could see cinema searching first for the Conrad, Melville, Dostoevsky nexus with Ford Coppolla trying to borrow the meaning of *Heart of Darkness* for *Apocalypse Now* (a wild-goose chase of literary epithet and allusion leading from Conrad to James Frazier to T.S. Eliot to Jessie Weston and back again to Conrad), or even Andre Malraux's Grant in his *The Royal Way*, to a Vietnam experience.

Michael Cimino might as well have been making *Rambo* with all his military organization fantasy and fabrications, but war as suicide seems a legitimate existential concern, that is,

---

[18] Barry Wallenstein, *Unsettled Accounts,* The American Book Review, November- December 1985, p. 5.

when it isn't homicide. One of Cimino's obituaries said that when *Deer Hunter* was released, Cimino implied in various interviews that the story (credited to him and three other scribes) was autobiographical, or else based on tales he heard when he was part of a 1968 Green Beret medical unit in Vietnam (nobody who was a former Beret would refer to a "Green Beret medical unit"). A studio head said, when he heard the story, that "If Cimino had ever been a Green Beret, then he was a rutabaga." Cimino told this version to a *New York Times* writer before the movie's release in 1978 when she asked him if the *The Deer Hunter* was autobiographical. The truth is, Cimino was never in Vietnam, was never a Green Beret, and his military experience was limited to six months in the reserves in 1962. According to the obituary, other details of Cimino's life were later subject to scrutiny, criticism and re-evaluation, including his age and even his gender identity. He variously listed the year of his birth as 1939, 1943 and 1952, sometimes shifting the month. You can see how he would have qualified to make a Rambo film.

Why pick on Rambo? Because America turned it's combat lust to Sylvester Stallone seven years later when *Soldier of Fortune* magazine (June 1985) critiqued *Rambo: Part II* in "Sly Stands Up For Vietnam Vets," contending that this was the movie that finally got Vietnam right:

"It's about time. And it's about time someone in one of America's most influential industries spent the money and effort to get the technical details right. Stallone has done that…"

What world did that happen in? Stories made up by the same dreamer artists writing for *Soldier of Fortune* as those writing for the movies, and all of them Michael Cimino Green Berets, Seals, Force Recon, or commandos of some kind.

After seeing Oliver Stone's *Platoon* in 1988, a war story of another type, H. experienced a different kind of hallucination. The concept that there is some kind of generic Vietnam War/atrocity story—if you weren't telling that story yourself you had to be commenting on somebody else's war tribulation like a messed-up veteran on thorazine in group therapy, or a writing course about the history of American atrocity in the Vietnam war as a punch bowl.

You couldn't see *Platoon* around Christmas, 1987, if you were a former grunt who did time in

Vietnam, and not be recalled by noises and colors that conjured up a land now lost. H. was thinking about all that green, everything olive drab; the canteen covers, the dull enameled curves of Hueys, B-3 units, polystyrene claymores, H-harnesses, watch bands, the buttressed mangroves with lime waters swirling through gothic root systems and tangled lianas and the almighty wall of the forest that seemed, for the foot-worn infantry, an enveloping *limbus fatuorum* of exotic and deadly beauty.

But, technical faithfulness does not vouchsafe dramatic realism and there is much of the temporary liar and visionary in Stone's remembrance of his war, regardless of the number of Oscars of approval and testimonials to the contrary. Indeed, the encomiums and awards collected by this film would be surprising in light of the message, if we did not already know the history of *Apocalypse Now* and *The Deer Hunter* and understand the hair-trigger reliability of American criticism.

And what was the message? It was disconcerting at best and was certainly not one, if it were his own personal story, H. would have wanted disseminated to the general public. The experiences and script of *Platoon* did not take their life from Stone's own service in 1967-1968, with B Company, 3rd Battalion, 21st Infantry, 25th Infantry Division, in which Stone was wounded and decorated once for heroism in combat (Bronze Star for Valor), so much as it bleeds life from a montage of actions which occurred over a number of years in Vietnam (and hence the "punchbowl" reference). One could discern a little of the worst of the 1st Cavalry experiences in Ia Drang Valley and LZ English, nuances of the Marine pacification effort in the north, the 101st Airborne Division fighting in the A Shau Valley (Ap Bia Mountain), individual battles spaced out over five years of the First Infantry Division, the 173rd Airborne Brigade, and the 1st Cavalry Division, and an overriding psychological atmosphere that can only have been drawn from the described actions of the troops of C Company, 1st Battalion, 20th Infantry, Americal Division at My Lai.

Out of the hundreds of thousands of actions involving U.S. troops in direct combat action, only a handful offered the circumstances which recreated the general atmosphere of *Platoon*. H. could say, as a former infantryman who served with one of the most decorated units in the modern history of American warfare, the 16th Infantry Regiment of the First Infantry Division, at generally the same time and place as Stone, that there was nothing about his own experience, other than the coincidence of geography, the hues of green and the Army, that recalled Stone's experience to him. H. said this because the players in Stone's film operated in a realm that imitated, in many ways, the allegorical and mythical landscapes of *The Pilgrim's Progress*, or the *Iliad*. The autobiographical Stone was tested in his actions at the Hill of Difficulty, the Valley of Humiliation, the Valley of the Shadow and the Doubting Castle. *Platoon*, like the *Iliad*, was the fictional counterpart of an historical verity. As Richard Lattimore assessed the relationship of the *Iliad* and Homer, so too *Platoon* and Stone; from the event, the legend, from the legend, the Stone.

But the archetypal journey in *Platoon* is an inversion of the Christian and mythic response in *Progress* and the *Iliad*. In *Platoon*, man did not struggle to ensure his place in Heaven, or history, but progressed, ineluctably, to a place in Hell and a victory for nothingness. While all may have a nightmare, the Vietnam infantry experience will never quite live up to the punic confabulations and downward anamorphosis *Platoon* represents on the screen. Robert Graves, the British poet and classicist, who wrote the defining autobiography of the trench warfare experience of World War I in *Goodbye To All That*, described the culminating syndrome of all war, exaggeration:

"The memoirs of a man who went through some of the worst experiences of trench warfare are not truthful if they do not contain a high proportion of falsities. High explosive barrages will make a temporary liar or visionary of anyone; the old trench-mind is at work in all over-estimation of casualties, "unnecessary" dwelling on horrors, mixing of dates and confusion between trench rumors and scenes actually witnessed."

When Stone recalled the infantry experience as incoherent and a model of varying degrees of panic, he noted something true, yet it is a truth that was not admirable, or advertisable, and was an exception when it was carried to its extreme as in *Platoon*. What is seen portrayed in *Platoon* are the actions of the *faex populi* and not the tragic heroes of Sparta and Troy.

There are two very powerful facts that critics and many of the participants in the Vietnam War overlooked in their visionary assessments of this particular past in American charity. One has to do with the 2.7 million American logistical servicemen and women who served in Vietnam and the other is found in the myriad personality of the Vietnam War itself. When people began believing *Platoon* as a model and revelation in the conduct of American military in the War, when youth and the uninitiated in American began believing this particular vision of light moving on a wall was a documentarian scroll of a collective experience, Vietnam veterans were, of all people, to be most pitied.

But H. had side-tracked from the intended discussion of literature because of film, even though film can be a literary response in cinematic terms. What of the literature? H. believed that the world hadn't seen a literature out of this war reminiscent of Sartre, Malraux, Conrad, Melville, or Dostoevsky (yet). In fact, the best writing by occidentals about the East in the last century has been penned by Englishmen; Orwell's *Burmese Days*, Anthony Burgess' *Malayan Trilogy* (*Time For a Tiger, The Enemy in the Blanket*, and *Beds in the East*), and working west, Paul Scott's *Raj Quartet* and Lawrence Durrell's *Alexandria Quartet* (four novels as oriental as any to be found). War is not necessarily a subject matter in all of these books, but beauty and a violent geography play large roles.

It is not coincidental, then, that the one book about Vietnam which grapples with what the Norwegian Academy calls *djupsinnig,* profound meaning in translation (the Academy never recognized it in him though), was by an Englishman and predated the American war by some five to ten years. Graham Greene's *The Quiet American* was a profound literary response to an Indochina in 1951-1954 menaced by the same war in the shadows America would come to know so well later. Greene, disenchanted with Malaya, fell in love with Indochina (Vietnam). He said in his *Ways of Escape:*

"The spell was first cast, I think, by the tall elegant girls in white silk trousers; by the pewter evening light on flat paddy fields, where the water buffaloes trudged fetlock deep with a slow primeval gait; by the French perfumeries in the rue Catinat, the Chinese gambling houses in Cholon; above all by the feelings of exhilaration which a measure of danger brings to the visitor with a return ticket: the restaurants wired against grenades, the watchtowers striding along the roads of the southern delta with their odd reminders of insecurity: "*Si vous betres arretes ou attaques en cours de routes, prevenez le chef du premier poster important.*"[19]

The country and landmarks were all recognizable; Saigon, Tay Ninh, Eurasian beauty, drugs, Nui Ba Den, brothels. There was much in Greene's novel that informed the American journalist Michael Herr's later writing in *Dispatches*. Green employed the first person (a journalist) and forms of reportage. Greene said that there was more reportage in *The Quiet American* than in any other novel he had written. In reflecting on Michael Herr's Vietnam portraits in *Dispatches* and Greene's Indochina writing one could see a *deja vu* quality. Herr, like Greene, moved back and forth between the countryside and the city. Herr's sighting of Vietnamese students at La Pagode and Brodards leafing *pliede* editions of French classics was reminiscent of a diary excerpt in which Greene found two of his translated novels in an opium house (*Le Ministere de la Peux* and *Roche de Brighton*). He paid 30 pilasters for a pipe and wrote a *dedicace* in each of the novels. But Greene's

[19] Graham Greene, *Ways of Escape, Simon and Schuster: New York, 1980, p. 161.*

writing was fiction, not reportage, and it recreated Vietnam in the way this current-day fascination with blood and guts of war has not.

In *The Quiet American*, it wasn't the story of love, war, the death of Pyle, and the detective inquiry that were so important to him since his 1966-1967 Vietnam. It was the way that the novel has come down over the years as prophetic of the doomed American involvement in Vietnam (beginning in 1946 and ending in 1975) and the reverberations of the wars of American generations since. Pico Iyer, an English, but American and Indian writer as well, hits on the fascination of this book for H.

"It also is a typically Greenian prophecy of what would happen 10 years later when U.S. troops would arrive, determined to teach a rich and complex place the latest theories of Harvard Square. Lyrical, enchanted descriptions of rice paddies, languorous opium dens and even slightly sinister Buddhist political groups are a lanterned backdrop to a tale of irony and betrayal. But that's not why I keep reading and rereading *The Quiet American*, like many of Greene's books, and have it always with me in my carry-on, a private bible. Certainly it's true that if you walk through modern

Saigon, as I have done, you can see Greene's romantic triangle playing out in every other hotel. And if you think about Iraq, Afghanistan, elsewhere, you see the outline of the same story."[20]

H.'s son-in-law wrote a book review of Greene's *The Quiet American* to bring his own experiences as a U.S. Marine professional of 23 years of service, several of them served in the Persian Gulf War, Iraq and Afghanistan, to an understanding of the Vietnam war. He found these convergences:

"I am a U.S. Marine veteran of the Persian Gulf War, and the Iraq and Afghanistan warfronts and have pondered ever since my service how they repeated the same political, military, and international strategy as those inheritors of Graham Greene's *The Quiet American* (Greene said somewhere that the only quiet American was a dead American). My father-in-law was a Vietnam veteran who served in Tay Ninh province, the setting of Chapter Two of the novel (the seat of the Cao Dao Temple under the shadow of the holy mountain visited by Fowler and Pyle; Fowler to

---

[20] Pico Iyer, The Disquieting Resonance of 'The Quiet American,' All Things Considered, NPR Radio, April 21, 2008.

interview the Pope of the Cao Dao faith). He revisited Saigon (or Ho Chi Minh City) and Vietnam several times after 1994 and always pointed out Greene's *The Quiet American* to me when we discussed the Persian Gulf, Iraq and Afghanistan. You can see *The Quiet American* in my wars in the serious nonfiction written both during and after. I am thinking of *The Forever War* by Dexter Filkins, *Hubris: The Inside Story of Spin, Scandal and the Selling of The Iraq War* by David Corn and Michael Isikoff, *Losing Small Wars: British Military Failure in Iraq and Afghanistan* by Frank Ledwidge, *Our Latest Longest War: Losing Hearts and Minds in Afghanistan* by Aaron B. O'Connell, *Directorate S: The C.I.A. and America's Secret Wars in Afghanistan and Pakistan* by Steve Coll, and first and foremost, *The Operators* by Michael Hastings (recently made into a movie, *The War Machine*, starring Brad Pitt as General McCrystal). And for the quagmire of Vietnam, the seminal works on the Vietnam War—-as the aforementioned books about our other wars prove—-witness that "Those who do not know history are doomed to repeat it" (*The Making of a Quagmire*, and *The Best and Brightest* by David Halberstam; *A Bright Shining Lie: John Paul Vann and America in Vietnam* by Neil Sheehan)."[21]

---

[21] Robert DuTremble, The Quiet American, A Book Review, May 2018.

Here is an irony. H. served his tour in Vietnam in the Iron-Triangle and the triple-canopy jungle towards the central border of Cambodia (called the Parrot's Beak). On only a few occasions did H. see any of the cities of Vietnam and he saw Saigon only three times. One would think that after spending thirteen months with Infantry and Recon experiencing combat at first-hand one would have all the material necessary to write a war novel, of one type, or another, good or bad.

But the opposite happened. War in the jungles, seemed, as time went by, to have been miniaturized. The heated ambience of city—Saigon in his experience—is magnified. H. was fascinated with a growing list of urban items. H. wanted to lay hands on those documents that described and recorded Saigon in a certain period of time; the betting program from Pho Tho horse track in Cholon, a train schedule for Saigon to Nha Trang, menus from every kind of restaurant, ads in the Daily scandal sheet, street maps, city directories, the phone book, and the concert schedule for August 1966 at the opera house. With all that in hand maybe one could begin to write about the war and, more importantly, about Vietnam. Not the Vietnam of

America, but the Vietnam identified by its own aromas, clamor, craftsmanship, industry, mimicry, art and adaptation.

It's a personal feeling about what real literature was composed of, and the measure of that for him was James Joyce's *Ulysses*. Joyce said to someone in a letter that *Ulysses* was Dublin; that if Dublin should one day disappear, one would only have to read his book to recreate the place. H. wanted to see the book written about war-time Saigon that, as lost as it was, would serve as a blueprint to resurrect not only Saigon, but an American experience in Vietnam. Edna O'Brien, a Dublin admirer of Joyce, said in the biography she wrote about him when she was in her twenties, that the magic of *Ulysses* was that "Dublin was not merely a backdrop for its characters, but had everything as a city that it's Irish characters had in human richness. No other writer," she said, "so effulgently and so ravenously recreated a city."

To H. the East didn't seem a simple place. It was not the Congo where Marlow played Stanley to Kurz's Livingston. It was not a voyage out with wooden planking between mankind and a watery womb. The English writers H. mentioned earlier captured the ornamental splendor and decadence of the East better than most for they were committed to live in a country for years (as civil servants, merchants or soldiers) and saw firsthand how the East imposed itself on a life, on a story, on ideas. The story may be everything, but the story about Vietnam must take place near the ubiquitous ads for the best little Chinese bath across the avenue from Dr. Chub's where one can be treated for VD and GU infections after five pm. To confirm Wallenstein's further remarks about inventing fiction in Vietnam's literature:

"From many of the veterans who are now writing about their experiences, inventing fictions which even better approximate their experiences, we hear the comment, 'There's a lot of crap written about Nam,' and, 'No one has yet put the record straight.' The impenetrableness of this war, even many years after the fact, contributes to this urgent desire to write about it and explain."

The big impetus for all of this Vietnam writing and remembering probably had to do with the kind of memory the war inspired in us. It is tactile memory; a particular recall is not motivated out of some complicated ratiocination, but by an aroma, a noise, a sight, even a taste. One was left with the impression that memory had been engraved on the convoluted symmetry of the brain; a lost geography in holograph. There is a phenomenon where photographic plates upon which holographic images have been imprinted in three dimensions by lasers in diffractive patterns—when broken—record on each splinter the clear and untarnished image of the whole subject. There is an ominous thunder and the sudden spit of afternoon rain; banana fronds and palms gently sway in a terraced valley at the end of the mind.

So, there were reasons for H. why many were dissatisfied with the literary responses to the Vietnam experience and much of it had nothing to do with literature as a scalpel. There was, in much of the writing about the war, an affection for promulgating certain myths about combat, about confrontation. What is most detestable about soldier of fortune mentalities in writing and film seems to be more genre than exception. Much of the writing about this war does trigger deep meditation, but if it is ever to rank with the grim probing of Sartre, the whiteness of Melville, the underground of Dostoevsky, and the dark interior of Conrad, it will have to trigger, also, our deepest admiration.

Search for Joseph Conrad all you will but H. felt we have a different writing after this war, about this war and because of this war from Americans. And there are a couple of things about Vietnam writing, fiction and nonfiction, which seem wrong, even false. One is the way all writing about the Vietnam experience, unless it's historiography, seems to fall into the rite of passage mode, or confessional, tales of suffering, deliverance, but not so much, enlightenment. The other is the impression given by writers, whether they are novelists, or historians, that everyone who served in Vietnam was a combat soldier and experienced the hardships and trials of combat (but this may be phenomena transported from all wars).

And because of this Vietnam War Narrative, war writing propagated the biggest myth about the Vietnam war, the tale that the war experience itself was generic, that every one of the three plus million, or more, who received cut orders and showed up in country underwent this rite of passage. The truth about any expeditionary military force was much different. The formula for service in a war arena went something like this. Less than ten out of every one-hundred soldiers (one-hundred thousand out of a million) were assigned a combat arms MOS (Military Occupational Specialty) and then there was a pecking order existing among combat arms roles; cross-border operands in Studies and Observation Group (Marine Force Recon, Navy Seals, Army Special Forces) sat on the tip of this pyramid of bad-ass and carried out, by far, the most dangerous combat missions in the war venturing into and among superior enemy strongholds in Cambodia, Laos and North Vietnam; next were the LRRPs (Long Range Reconnaissance Patrols) and Rangers who carried out all in-country reconnaissance (LRRPs evolved into Ranger units in Vietnam in an organizational table change in 1969); then the straight-leg and airborne infantry (Army and Marine) carrying out large unit search and destroy missions seeking massed-force confrontations with the enemy. The wing of Navy, Air Force, Army and Marine pilots shot down over enemy territory defined an entirely separate category of service and sacrifice. Everybody else in that ten percent should crowd in under these warriors as the foundation blocks of this combat pecking order.

What were the ninety out of every hundred (nine-hundred thousand out of one million) remaining Soldiers, Sailors, Marines, and Airmen doing? Support and logistics. Literally thousands of specialities divided among five major military branches, from cook to photographer, from preacher to teacher. What does that mean? Well, it means that any one of them might, in the face of the random and unpredictable nature of a war with fluid borders, be in the wrong place at the wrong time, but that is not what most of them faced or expected to face. They had a better chance of winning the Chinese lottery. Many of these rear-echelon servants lived like Kings in paradise and anyone in the top enlisted ranks (E-8, E-9), or in the officer class over the rank of Major, was not exposed to the "Great Generic Vietnam War" experience, if it could be helped. But you read the history of this war and not only does every one of the 3 million, or more, who served in Vietnam over a 16 year period barely suppress screams but also, it appeared, the ones who got left at home.[22] H.

---

[22] *See* Fred Turner, *Echoes of Combat*, Anchor Books Doubleday: New York, 1998. This is a book that posits, among its premises, that the Vietnam War was a horror for the American participants and the

noticed once, in *Harper's* (June 1984, "Barely Suppressed Screams," by C.D.B Bryan, author of the nonfiction, *Friendly Fire),* the reference to a formula appearing in writing about the Vietnam War experience Bryan called the "Generic Vietnam War Narrative." In referring to the novels, memoirs, collections, journalistic treatments, and nonfiction accounts about Vietnam he fitted them all into that universal hell that was Vietnam. He even ended his essay with these inclusionary words:

"Because of the overt way the Vietnam War so deeply touched so many lives, the literature it spawned reflects an immediate outcry at the explosiveness of its evil. The Great Vietnam War Novel, in its exploration of all the subtleties and deceptions, will have to vent screams **we still suppress."**

"We still suppress." H. wondered what war experience could the writer of this essay be suppressing? The experience of researching and writing the book *Friendly Fire* (a tragic story "of

---

American people at home, every one of them, not to mention the later grouping, Viet Guilt veterans.

a nation at war with itself")? The same question held true for all those other writers referred to who composed the voice of Vietnam literature, the voice that was a "barely suppressed scream."

H.'s reaction to this feeling by writers about the war and writers about writers about the war that Vietnam was a collective horror was surprise. It's certain that Vietnam, as have most arenas of combat, settled in a young man or woman's mind a bit bigger than life, by hearsay, or by experience. The magnitude of the disaster, the proportion of an atrocity, the weight of a culpability, the breadth of a river under fire, all came down in time a mite bigger, a degree or more awe-inspiring (*c.f.* Robert Graves). Vietnam writing tended to paint for us, despite what statistics and good sense tell us, this war as a single battlefield of the past where city, paddy, forest and stream were strategic sectors in an enfilading fire; where the paradigmatic grunt, the dog soldier, was exposed for 11 long years and there was hell to pay. There was also the tendency, even if H. didn't buy into this version, to pay some kind of lip service to it, much as one does to a tradition; take his hat off at a funeral, or stand for the national anthem.

No exaggeration is too great for war but the country then becomes a kind of caricature. Trips H. took back to Vietnam in the 90's changed all of that for him. H. saw occasionally the paintings of Vietnam he experienced in 1966-67, but without the fear factor. He could now drive down a stretch of highway once called "Claymore Alley" (Highway 13) at two in the morning with moon full above rice paddies and holy mountain and, if he had to, stop and piss in a rice paddy. Safety seemed to make the beauty of the country all the more manifest. That was surprising, for the beauty of Vietnam was never far from mind no matter how deadly the encounter. It was also disconcerting to hear how ugly the place was where so many did not encounter the deadly.

The Vietnam War changed the people and the country every minute, every hour, every day. The war varied according to geography, according to service. Each military and civilian assignment affected or directed one's experience in Vietnam. The Naval and Marine night fliers of Operation Rolling Thunder over North Vietnam recall a different war than the Air Force pilots who flew ground support missions in the south. Veterans of SMAG, TAG and SOG forces won't recognize the Vietnam of a Third Field Hospital technician.

Vietnam could be the best of times and the worst of times, according to the logistical formula given above. Every *Rumor of War*, or *Fields of Fire*, demanded twenty travelogues on Saigon and environs, twenty illuminations of the night life in Cholon, twenty diaries of foreign diplomats in the style of Jon Beames and twenty chronicles fixing the protocol of black-marketeering by province. Where were the compilations that concern themselves with the sociology and the anthropology of the American Vietnam?

The rampant industry of retrospective analysis and fictionalizing was a complicated affair and appeared to be as much a search for consensus as a forum for storytelling. Sociologists *qua* anthropologists spoke of war and its accumulations as class-conflict, and pitted black against white, misfits against idealists, commies against democrats, and good against evil. The military and the media reenacted major deceits of the war (Sisyphus pushing that rock) and the final estimates, like agents of *Tlon, Uqbar, Orbis Tertius*, repeated in new and disturbing ways, the Five-O'clock follies (*Westmoreland v. CBS, Bush v. CBS, U.S. v. NY Times, Washington Post v. U.S., et al*).

Where were the poets (no Homers, Sassoons, Graves, Owens, or Jarratts versifying about "that" war, or were there) while other literary types were cranking out a 100 new novels a month about it? Politicians, unable to remember the lessons of war, were doomed forever to begin each new incursion in diplomatic kindergarten. And having brought up the guilt suffered by those who didn't serve, a symptomania that followed mankind through all wars from Peloponnesia to Afghanistan, the introduction of a malady which may well be included now in the *Diagnostic and Statistical Manuel* under "Viet Guilt." Coined in the 1980's, James Fallows, Bob Greene, Fred Turner, Christopher Buckley and others explicated this malady for us in nostalgic parentheses on class, duty, honor, country. It seemed that a certain segment of America missed the war and now they miss the war.

The Vietnam consensus was akin to the Oracle of Delphi which neither spoke plainly nor concealed, but revealed through hints. Vietnam was being revealed through a series of fascinations which follow the example of fads. We shaped our memory of Vietnam with diagnostic indicators from the *Neurological Quarterly*, or from panel and line number on a black marble wall in the nation's capital. This recognition was epicyclic; the year of the MIA, the year of the POW, the year of memorialization, of parades, the 10th anniversary, the 20th anniversary, the "Welcome Home," the 40th anniversary.

If H. went back 60 years, he would've witnessed something amazing, something that was never mentioned. You could drive up into the highlands of Central Vietnam to Dalat, which was once the former playground of Indochina and the summer home of Vietnamese kings, a location described by Helen Churchill Candee, an American writer traveling Indochina in the early 1900's, as "That amazingly beautiful health-resort in the mountains." Norman Lewis, the British travel writer, on the other hand, said in the 1930's that it was an uninspired imitation of subalpine atmosphere: "It looked like a drab little resort in *Haute Savoie*, developed by someone who had spent a few years as vice-consul in Shanghai."[23] But it was the surprising history involving this resort, home of kings, which could have been incorporated in a dark comedy, or a light tragedy. Looking east from the golf course driving range, or

[23] Norman Lewis, *A Dragon Apparent*, 1951.

where it used to be, close by where the Salon *de The*, Crillon Grill and the chic Shanghai Bar once stood, reactor room footings and columns began to take shape in 1961. Photos of President Ngo Dinh Diem, U.S. Ambassador Nolting, and Dr. Ban of the Atomic Energy Office placed them at construction ceremonies with the hive-work of reactor columns standing behind them like unfinished Olympic stanchions. A nuclear reactor, rising one-hundred feet in the sky, was constructed in 1961 "in increments of approximately 15 cm by hand hoisting the concrete by rope and a scoop holding approximately 1.1/2 shovels full of concrete."[24] In the Bronze age of American atomic research, the U.S. was seen busily installing a breeder reactor in a haven of terrorists and guerillas.

H. thought that those circumstances would have resulted in something far more apocalyptic than a rite of passage journal, but most don't even know the reactor existed. H. never saw it mentioned in film, book or documentary. H.

---

[24] Republic of Vietnam Information Printing Office, *Seven Years of the Ngo Dinh Diem Administration,* 1954-1961, 1962. Diem had his "achievements" recorded in this obscure report. This astonishing volume is dedicated to heralding the "total liberation of man as an individual."

wondered how Robert Ludlum, or Frederick Forsyth, hadn't got ahold of this congratulatory publication, apparently printed in a once and only edition of five, and made some Bournes and dogs of war out of it. None of those multi-volume film documentarists discovered this lodestone either, or weren't excited enough by it to investigate.

H. said "multi-volume documentarists" because for four decades he had heard gravel-voiced narrators who sounded like Bud Greenspan's David Perry over the fragmented décolletage of a misty tree line in An Loc, or Mai Loc. The first in this practice was a 13-hour pasticcio retelling 100 years of Vietnam history with emphasis on the last 11 and the telling was done in cinema vignettes which half-the-time posed high-ranking officials of the plot sitting on royal red leather discussing, with cigarette hands, "The War." It was an era and ambience lived out in quaint travelogue, choreographed dialogue and garish and ill-lighted 16mm color-print with fortuitous camera angles. The last was by Ken Burns (*The Vietnam War*), and another 13 hours of 30 years of combat employing his widely used technique of embedding still photographs in motion pictures, displayed with slow zooming and panning effects and fading transitions between frames.[25]

But H. did not see, in all the hours of documentation, Prince Bao Dai cavorting in mufti amongst the harlots of Le Dao street in humid Saigon. Nor Prince Norodom Sihanouk, honored neighbor, on a blue-marbled Lu Gia balustrade in madras shirt singing his lyrics to that well-loved, but little-known ballad, *Regret.* No echoes of *Gymnopedies* commingling with the gurgling turn of the Vu Gia about the irrigation wheel of a pauper Annamite. Vietnam was suited to such displays and belonged as much to the pen of Greene as the camera of a Satyajit Ray, David Lean, or Akira Kurosawa.

And H. did not see, as he had witnessed, Vietnamese workers flitting from row to row of rubber with double buckets shouldered on balancing poles emptying latex bowls and renotching the dark-trunked trees. Through the long rows of rubber H. had seen, in the dappled light a Citroen, or Renault, motoring down a

---

25 Apparently borrowed from a 1957 Canadian documentary about the Klondike gold rush although there were more photos, film, videotape and home-movies in this war than the Civil War, WW I, WW II, and Korea combined.

laterite road carrying the plantation owner back to his villa for lunch, or siesta.

Documentary memories? H. remembered Nguyen van Bao, gutshot, resting pale arms in an unclouded pool. A white hyacinth spread open on the opaque surface, its red mouth like the crimson gash of van Bao's wound. And the pool clouding, fed by thin rivulets of blood; golden carp turning and turning in the crimson stain; *in hoc corpus meum*. H. recalled the market streets glutted with the fumes of glycerine, sesame and fishes.; the rattle and hum of Renault cabs droning through puddle water standing by glum doorways. Upstairs, and down, foreigners about arranging *liaisons avec Vietnammiennes*. Young girls on bicycles pedaling by with ao-dais fluttering long petals to the wind. Indoors; bargirls, au-dais tucked chastely round cushioned buttocks, speaking of the boat cuisine on the Basac in Chan Doc, or Truyen nom.

And music? When H. heard Debussy or Ravel, he heard Vietnam. In 1966, before H. knew who Ravel was, he heard the strains of a strange music coming out the window of a French plantation house near the sprawling Michelin Rubber Plantation at Quon Loi. As H. later learned, that strange music was one of the seminal pieces of French impressionism. It fixed an impression on a young man, enough to trigger misguided attempts at poetry. H.'s first attempt was inspired by that very geography of it, "Quon Loi." Remembering in 1975 this impressive plantation near the Cambodian border (part of the French Michelin rubber empire) triggered the feeling that must inspire all poets, and like ballet, or opera, H. thought that Ravel's beautiful music should inform his overwrought representations:

It is there upon the lawns like a delicate smile,
Eugenie Grandet, Paul Dormer, perch in a
window pile–
Miroirs echo upon the whited tiles.
Marched from the buttressed mangroves
of Tay Ninh,
The haunted warriors eager for the fruits
of sin
Enter Quon Loi, infibulated village of Cochin.
At the keys, an historical woman bends,
levant airs and dances sift through
moving fronds;
Casuarina, tomentosa, and the golden tranh.
The stuccoed Frenchman's house,
his solitude,
Mocks at the hollow men, the hollow few.

H. knew that it was too much French music and literature in too short a period of time, and a big dose of T.S. Elliot. This house/home of whited tiles where something or other was upon the lawns like a delicate smile (a reference to an obscure line in Jean P. Sartre's *Reprieve*) was the central pavilion of what had once been a superb villa owned by a French rubber industry magnate in An Loc. It was a lush antipode pointing toward Cambodia with its own airfield and surrounded by tall rubber trees, a nine-hole golf course, several manor houses, and an Olympic-size swimming pool with one and three meter diving boards. Smaller native dwellings dotted a laterite road winding through the thick stand of rubber trees toward the larger town of An Loc. The central house was finished in bleached stucco with a terra cotta roof in the Riviera style. The French still administered the property in some precarious contract with the South Vietnamese, and apparently, those other Vietnamese, the enemy.

Somewhere in the area heavy buckets of rubber latex were processed. H. remembered his squad, or platoon, bivouacking in the ruins of an old latex mill. It too was surrounded by the orange and ivory Riviera construction seen everywhere in the south. Years later, the memories of these places, like a magnet, drew H. back to Vietnam. The more his memories refined, the more he thought that no country, or its war, was more suited to literature and film than Vietnam. The flora and fauna flashed in gold, emerald and saffron. Nowhere could a civilization be as easily identified by its aromas, clamor, linguistic patterns, craftsmanship and industry as the Vietnamese with its accents of French and Americanism. Vietnam, for the interested, could most accurately be raised from a project of research that ignored military situation reports, after-action reports, daily journals and lessons learned. H. found it instead in a volume on Southeast Asian cookery, a list of Indian spices, Jarvit's Guide to Botanical Plants, the morning line for the Pho Tho horse track, a train schedule for My Tho/Bien Hoa, or a register of herbs on display at a local apothecary. References to a volume on orographic rains could shed new light on the meaning and majesty of the pouring monsoons that dominated the cycles of Vietnamese existence. Tomes of military detritus existed on unit heraldry, uniforms, labels and containers of every beer and alcoholic concoction, allied heraldry, weapons, armaments and materials which individually held more interest than all the tales of firefights.

To recreate Saigon simply go to one of the English-language newspapers published daily (Saigon had thirty newspapers, three in English, two in French). Full of classified delectations in a garbled grammar reminiscent of James Joyce's "Oxen of the Sun" parody of the progress of English style (and language), they recomposed the streets, machinery, idioms and culture of a fabulous era in this exotic land:

Quick as the wind that often stirred the banana trees with utter ferocity in his home town, where his favorite horse had died an alcoholic death, the smart copper jumped on the thief just as the sinister individual was about to ride on his faithful vehicle. (Saigon Post, 1966)

A story in the Saigon Daily News interpreted a recent Buddhist immolation:

A 16-year old apprentice monk soaked himself with gasoline and burned himself to death. He was believed to have taken his life out of discontent with his superior, who had reproached him of listening too much to radio music.

From the personal ads, love in the afternoon:

Beautiful V.N. lady (38 years old single well built) wishes to make friend with white men. Contact directly at 183/4 hem 2, Cao Thang, Phu Nhuan, Gia Dinh (near Phu-Nhuan market) at noon.

Beloved Dr. N.T. Chuc, Baylor University, advertised treatments for VD and GU infections, 5:00-8:00 p.m. at 87 Phat Diem, Saigon (why in the evening?), and one could always find the ubiquitous ads for the only Turkish bath in town: “Enjoy private steam tub with pretty girls massage” (Phan Than Gian). And the menus are piled in oil-stained memory; Maxim’s Milan, Hotel Victoria and every Vietnam Garden slinging Nigiri sushi, Peking duck, spring roll and fried rice.

More and more the mystery of the crowd, the erected city and all its attendant constructions beckoned in the story of the American in Vietnam. Less and less the revelation of combat which sketched the rifleman, the platoon leader, the medic and the enemy filtering a story of woe and terror back through the eyes of the reader. Train schedules (if the trains were running) the Daily

Racing Form, the city map, a thousand and one documents that reestablished the symmetry and existence of a city and country some 9,000 miles distant, one which H. barely rubbed elbows with but the more he read about it, the more elephantine it had become. Perhaps it was the monstrosity of a city with two and one-half million people that could lend itself to the mythical and to symbolism; a palette of many cultures and many sins, not to mention a zoo and botanical garden. In this city everything seemed possible.

And if the jungle must finally be invoked, you want a war story without the war, one about an odyssey that avoids confrontations and starts like Homer's with encounters with lotus-eaters assorted apparitions, perhaps a cannibal, devils, winds, rains and fair weather, as war and life are always configured—Marlow going up the Congo River in 1898, or an American band of soldiers carrying out a lazy recon in Tay Ninh province in 1967.

So, the jungle could be as magical as the city, a kind of cathedral hidden from the common pilgrim requiring a crusade into purple prose. After H. and his band of brothers careened to a landing zone, a grassy savannah appeared in the jungle like a blight. Part of a staggered formation of eight or ten,

H. moved slowly through a maze of grasses and broken trees, guns perched over ammo packs dangled from canvas harnesses fitted loosely to sweated green. The jungle stood about the opening in tower walls with each dark gap between gnarled trees a door of entry and of exit. H. trudged into the great forest, ponderous steps and conversation drowned by an infernal stammering. Golden light threaded into the jungle roof filtered on occasion to the jungle floor, or silhouetted an angled column of mangrove, or lim. Fine dust displayed itself in dance, moving through the beams of penetrating light which appeared shaken in a dry rain from the canopies infested with sputtering monkeys and shrieking birds.

Vines and creeping lianas projected to and from an arching ceiling of green falling unkempt on warted trunks and moss upholstered granite protruding from the festered soil that leeched at the black gum of H.'s boots. Water from oaken reservoirs and hidden vessels seeped, giving the molded interior a sheen of glazed sponge or cancroid naugahyde. What little of the solar message passed corrupted itself in chitinous plant and vegetable insect, in malignant sores and running boils that erupted from a raw opening of rock and peat and meandered deeper into a mausoleum of exotic scents, of velvet jade and nitrous aether.

Through each new door of onyx an eruption and soon another thunder which subdued the shrieks and moans of the ceiling dwellers. Cascades of paregoric spilled in smooth streams over worn shards of marble and limestone, cut through the mossed carpet, dived under rotted mangrove and clumped bamboo, crested carbuncles and wens swollen with fungal pus and coursed a feral way to a hidden styx which, bloated, drained waters from a past that, no doubt, included this earth's first cooling rains.

And H. in this band of brothers moved through intermittent rows of plantation rubber and heavy growths of mango, ironwood, sal and sandal in the chattering rain forest stretching from Tay Ninh to the savage rim of Cambodia. They marched through the night, rows of heavily weaponed soldiers followed at armlength the phosphorescent flow of cystomeria leaves taped to the skull of hats, or pinned to shirts and backpacks. It was a dark processional marching in luminescent ornamentation toward a green encounter chanting, in this far-flung year, the chorus of Agamemnon:

Continuous drizzle from the sky,
Dews from the marshes
Rotting our clothes, filling
Our hair with lice.[26]

They carried the body of a fallen warrior. The jungle with spawning lianas reaching out in the shadows to take new root, whispering ferns, and crawling moonlight orchids transported the column to a Germanic wood, one where ancient hunters carried lean and bloodied stag and pig on shouldered staves; skaldic singers laden with franklins and linden shields. A light mist oozed on the jungle floor where heated tendrils and pulsing epiphytes met the cold-filtered starlight. The screams of panthers returned them to the aloes of Tay Ninh. And as dawn sidled its way through last imaginations, they came again into the long and curving aisles of hevea. The slim dark trees with seagreen canopies covered the morning infantry like the tearlet arches of a cathedral ceiling. A bevy of green sacristans, they slowly wended their way to the altar, morning cigarettes trailing

[26] *The Agamemnon,* Aeschylus, 458 B.C.E., Translated by D.E.A. Morehead.

bright smoke plumes in swing-step, like holy censors dangled from ragged soutanes.

Coming out of triple-canopied forest H. left darkness to stride on the edge of paradise. Cortez said, as he marched his hidalgos from Iztapalapa toward the splendor of Tenochtitlan, that he was living an enchanted vision from the *Tale of Amadis;* 20th century soldiers walking in his footsteps. Terraced paddy land spread before a rising hillock of jungle and meandered toward an Eden. Grazing beasts of the field, round-haunched and glistening, stood knee-deep in paddy water as dark urchins splashed between submerged fetlocks. Papaya, pineapple, mango, banana; an explosion of flowering plants and fruits emerged from the watery edge to mingle with the gleaming peninsulas of jungle. When black clouds ringleted the forest back and spilled in the afternoon heat sudden rain, needle-shoots of rice gleamed from spasms of brown water and the gelatin fronds of banana, coconut and mango poised in collimated green from lime to jade. Paddy, field, great forest and mountain blended one with the other down the contour of the valley and the light falling unbroken, the light behind a cirrus stream, and the light shifting through remnant tufts of cloud, moved in concentricity to the East in an ever-changing coition of radiance and shadow.

III – Through A Glass Darkly

In February 1994, about two weeks after the Clinton Administration lifted the economic embargo of Vietnam, and shortly after Tet (Vietnamese New Year), H. returned to Vietnam for the first time since his tour of duty in the U.S. Army's First Infantry Division in 1966-67. A former Special Forces A Detachment commander of H.'s, Dan Thompson, from Colonial Heights, Virginia, arranged the trip with a Vietnamese friend, Minh (taking his family back to Saigon/ Ho Chi Minh City for the first time since their midnight departure 18 years earlier), who was making his first millions in San Francisco in the new cell-phone industry. Dan used H. as a pathfinder for a quick tour of the south country of H.'s service and Minh as a guide in Saigon. From here, in a week, Dan was heading up north to revisit the demilitarized zone (17th Parallel) where he had run cross-border operations from a launch site east of Laos and just south of North Vietnam called Mai Loc, and then see a mystical geography called Marble Mountain near Danang.

H. flew in from Seoul on Asiana Flight 361, after twenty plus years of R&R. It was the dead of the night. Ho Chi Minh City, once Saigon, was lit up 100,000 Chinese lantern-watts and unparceling below now they had dropped under cloud cover and began a final approach to Tan Son Nhut Airport. H. wanted to experience again, with the knowledge gleaned in almost three decades of rumination, Vietnam. But mostly he came back to see the mystical mountain that had loomed large in his memory since he left this place and to discover if an oasis still existed at the end of a long and dusty road.

H. passed through the turnstiles of Tan Son Nhut airport again and stepped into the heat and humidity of the Vietnam night. To his right, somewhere in dim terminal lights, was the gravesite of Camp Alpha where all U.S. ground troops once processed to their separate assignments throughout Vietnam. To H.'s left, the ghosts of Seventh Air Force Headquarters. To his front, derelict streets that once cloistered the MACV Headquarters Compound and Annex, the brain-trust of U.S. Command and Control, or at least the middle peduncle of cerebellum, left an unimpeded view of the night.

The U.S. embargo was lifted weeks prior to the trip and all of the warnings *qua* fears about official harassment and constabulary corruption would be proven unfounded, except for the three hours checking through customs because H. didn't understand directions so well after 30 years away. Things had changed, it seemed, and what was noticeable was the paucity of officialdom everywhere, unless you went looking for it. Military uniforms were scarce except in the service of fee collection at battle memorials and museums designated for national consumption (Tunnels of Cu Chi, Khe Sanh, Ia Drang Valley). In Ho Chi Minh City, traffic police were in regular evidence, but nowhere the sound of alarms or sirens. A secret cease/desist order must have circulated when the embargo was lifted and its message lighted the way to the farthest flung outposts of socialism, north and south, east and west—"Lay off the tourists."

Early in the trip H. had arranged for transportation to Tay Ninh City as Thompson had agreed to accompany him there before he headed north to Danang. It is the Tay Ninh of violent battle in the late 60's and the city and cathedral that appeared in the 1958 version of *The Quiet American.* It was a noticeable place long before the war if for nothing more than the cathedral that resembled a Disney wet dream and marked the seat of the Cao-Dai religion in Vietnam. The British travel writer, Norman

Lewis, said in the 50s that "from a distance it appeared to be the monstrous result of marriage between a pagoda and a southern baroque church but at close range was the most outrageously vulgar building ever to have been erected with serious intent."[27]

The Cao-Dai faith was a 20th century invention, a phenomenon of eclecticism counting among its hierarchy of Saints Victor Hugo, Winston Churchill, Lao-Tse, Buddha and Jesus Christ. Worship took place between pink endragoned pillars and church iconography where the male Pope had female Cardinals and made prophecy from a ouija board.

But it was because of the mountain that the temple was built and the Black Virgin Mountain, or Nui Ba-Den, was a sight to behold:

". . . a single symmetrical mountain humps up suddenly from the plain, rising from what must be practically sea-level to 3000 feet. As there is not another hillock for fifty miles in any direction to break the flat and featureless monotony of Cochin-China, this darkly forested plumpudding silhouette is quite remarkable. In a part of the world where

---

[27] Lewis, Ibid.

every religion has its sacred mountain, such an eminence is obviously irresistible. Consequently, it has been since dimmest antiquity a place of revelation. Its slopes are said to be riddled with caves, both natural and artificial, housing at one time or other the cult objects of numerous sects."[28]

Departed from Ho Chi Minh City, they drove up Highway 22 and H. suddenly saw for the first time since 1967, the Black Virgin Mountain. It was a hazy, green bowler hat rising above a treeline southwest of Tay Ninh City. H. showed Thompson the 1958 movie *The Quiet American* starring Audie Murphy and Michael Redgrave before they set out on their Vietnam journey so Thompson would be familiar with the appearance of the mountain and the holy temple at the end of this road.

The moon was full on this day and the Black Virgin Mountain was crowded by vehicles and throngs of people at its base, acolytes who had come from afar in Vietnam to worship at the relics housed in and on the mountain for Tet, the celebration of the Vietnamese Lunar New Year. H. was disturbed by the heat, the dryness and

[28] Lewis, Ibid.

these memories and turned back to Tay Ninh City to witness another religious spectacle, this one housed in the cool marble and tile of the most outrageously vulgar building ever to have been erected with serious intent.

Their visit to the Cao Dai cathedral reprised the scenes shot almost 40 years ago in *The Quiet American.* While there was no festival parade, nor Audie Murphy and Michael Redgrave, the road leading into the holy complex was still packed dirt. In the film a long panning shot moved from the holy mountain to the temple buildings of the church and the cathedral. The grounds appeared as ugly and arid as they did on this day. Redgrave/Fowler saw Murphy/Pyle talking to a Vietnamese officer in the courtyard then a long panning shot followed him walking into the cathedral saying in voice-over, "A Walt Disney fantasia of the East. Dragons and snakes; no glass in the windows and everywhere the eye of God upon you." H. repeated this phrase to Thompson who later stood in the balcony surrounding the interior of the famous temple and did the *signum crucis*, sign of the cross, playing, he supposed, the Pope. Nervous about the all-seeing eye, they got in their ride and followed the self-same road driven by

Redgrave/Murphy in the movie, but without an unplanned stop at a French gun tower.

Ho Chi Minh City/Saigon was an old city and if one were even passing familiar with its modern history, one saw things that rang the memory bell constantly; architecture, streets, faces. It was a city with three personalities — Vietnamese, French, and American — although the American fingerprint was fast fading. Michael Herr wrote in *Dispatches* that Saigon had continuity:

"Saigon remained the repository and the arena, it breathed history, expelled it like toxin, Shit, Piss and Corruption. Paved swamp, hot mushy winds that never cleaned anything away, heavy thermal seal over diesel fuel, mildew, garbage, excrement, atmosphere."

The thermal seal covered an even bigger area now. This was a city of four or five million people and all of them appeared to have co-opted open air stalls on every available inch of sidewalk to vend everything from soup to transmissions; and if they weren't on the sidewalks they were on the roads, for the traffic is a river of klaxons, bells and horns that flowed unimpeded as if every driver were conferring with the *Tao*, and *T'ai Chi*; they went in with the descending vortex and come out with the ascending one.

H. submitted to a tributary to find *Dong Khoi* Street and the Majestic Hotel where he had booked. *Dong Khoi* Street was once the famous *Rue Catinat* mentioned in *The Quiet American*, and later the *Tu Do* Street of the American War reputation. It stretched from the landmark Notre Dame de Saigon cathedral and was flanked by the Rex Hotel, Continental Hotel, Opera House, National Assembly and, as one approached the quays of the Saigon River, the Majestic Hotel.

The Majestic was the grand hotel of French colony *fin de siecle* and after the French exit in 1954 the fifth-floor open-air bar looking out on the river boulevard and distant paddy fields of Nha Be was a favored drinking spot for journalists and Saigon commandos during the Vietnam War. From it now, drinking Heineken from cans beneath a trellis of pipe work hung with climbing vines surrounded by marble planters bursting with exotics and fronds, H. could see the Saigon Floating Hotel docked quayside on Ton Duc Than Boulevard. This Saigon moneymaker was a floating casino on Australia's Great Barrier Reef until going bankrupt in 1988. Towed to Saigon, it was the Asian Waldorf with room rates starting at US $175 a night, this in a country where the per capita income in 1991 was US $200 a year. 500 meters south a badly repainted Soviet built hydrofoil bobbed at tether awaiting its early morning jaunt up the Saigon River to the mouth of the Pacific and the peninsula of Vung Tau.

Looking over the balustrade at a convergence of famous streets and boulevards, H. could make out the urban synapse from cathedral to river Michael Herr described in 1967 and Graham Greene novelized in 1954. Pimps, street boys, money changers, child dakinis and cyclo hacks vied for the attention of every Western face on thoroughfares and what was available in 1966 seems to be offered in the same excess today.

After the 100 degrees of daylight, it was relaxing to sit on this shelf, feel the evening wind from off the river blowing warmly scents of frangipani into your face and listening to the clatter of the street below. For entertainment one could read the ubiquitous ads for Tiger Beer, Sony and Toshiba on giant billboards across the river.

The Majestic staff maintained a colonial demeanor outfitted in black and cranberry tuxedos.

The interior was cool, serene even under renovation. Through the doorless entrance one could see a bank of cyclo drivers ogling the exit of all lodgers and readying to launch an attack of incessant pandering. As H. exited or entered the Majestic, Italian, German, Russian French, Norse and even Nilo-Saharan language reverberated in an *Avenue des Babels*.

One evening H. was having a beer at the fifth-floor bar and trying to read from a paperback edition of Thomas Pynchon's *The Crying of Lot 49*. An Amerasian waiter asks H. in broken English what he was reading so he handed him the book. The waiter inspected it and asked, "What is W.A.S.T.E.?"

The jacket back blurb said:

Who is Oeidipa Mass? What is the strange legacy of her ex-lover Pierce Inverarity, California real-estate mogul, that first led her to the bizarre postal network called W.A.S.T.E. then to Genghis Cohen who likes his sex with the news on . . . ?

H. says he is rereading the book and hasn't got to the W.A.S.T.E part yet. "It stands for something like an idea or a company. Understand?"

The waiter nodded his head, "Yes, I know. Like CIA."

Yeah. Good analogy for Vietnam. Music drifts from a tape machine behind the bar. The waiter begins singing in a false basso lyrics from a Beatles tune:

"She lub you, yah, yah, yah . . . ."

He nodded. "The Beatles."

The waiter said, "Jo Yenno, Paa Marteen, Rank Stair. Good."

"Yes. George Harrison."

The waiter looked at him with a quizzical frown. H. began doing his best imitation of Elvis Presley singing "*Wise men say/Only fools rush in . . . .*" Behind the bar a waitress and barman began giggling. The waiter asked, "Are you American singer?"

IV – Shuffling Toward Phu Cuong

It was Wednesday, August 12, 1998. Four years later and H. is back for another go-around, the plane half-full this time, or half-empty, depending on how you look at planes, and life. Coming from Seoul, Korea, the flight was approaching Ho Chi Minh City and Tan son Knut airport when the pilot announced that KAL was pulling into in a 45-minute hold pattern over Ho Chi Minh City because Vietnam high government officials and pomp and circumstance called for a secured airport while foreign dignitaries were funneled into (out of) the city. KAL finally landed at four pm. H. checked through customs in all of five minutes flat. No fuss, no muss, unlike 1994, and arrived at the Saigon Hotel on Dong Du Street around five pm, a stone's throw from Dong Khoi Street. The new Caravelle twin tower, finished and unfinished, loomed over Dong Du and the Saigon Hotel. H. had a nice view toward the Saigon River although new high-rise construction was blocking much of the river. The Saigon Floating Hotel seemed to be missing. Hotel Bach Dang (former name of river street now named Ton Duc Thanh Street) was directly below on 33 Mac Thi Buoi Street, a forest of potted areca palms on the top floor. River ferries were crossing the Saigon river. A Laughing Red Cow Cheese advertisement, Chubb sign, LG with red disc logo, CARIC, and a Heineken billboard (neon) with a large red star sat across the river. These were all new, but the statue of Tran Hung Dao that fronted the Saigon Floating Hotel was still in place. It turned out they had towed the floating hotel to the Philippines, it apparently living out its life in laps around the Pacific.

Jet-lagged, H. walked down Dong Khoi about five blocks to the river front. H. went briefly into the renovated Majestic Hotel. They wanted $89 US for a room which was big drop from the $190 advertised. H. ended up about a block from his hotel at The Vietnam House on 95 Dong Khoi Street where he ordered giant prawn (grilled), shrimp-fried rice and a bottle of Beaujolais (George Tete?). A young Vietnamese women seated amongst fronds played an upright Yamaha with beautiful tone. She played music selected from a large brief case sitting atop the bench she sat on. H. sent a request for *Claire D'lune* which she played (she turned to it in one of her song books). She played it well but with hesitation; perhaps sight-reading it for the first time.

H. paid a Saigon Hotel driver, Mr. Nguyen Minh Hung, $28 for the day to take him around the city. H. changed $100 US to one million three-hundred eighty-five thousand Vietnam Dong. Thinking he couldn't count that in a day he went to Ho Hao Huong Street looking for TOP Hotel and H.'s driver and guide in 1994, Nhu Tran. A new and taller building was parked where the TOP once resided. He asked Hung to ask locals about the old hotel and Nhu Tran. They all shook their heads, "No. Never hear." Nhu was a Californian who invested in the hotel when expatriates were allowed back in country. They must have deported him, he sold out at profit, or they sent him to a reeducation camp.

H. told Hung that he wanted to go to Tay Ninh Province and the Black Virgin Mountain the next day. Hung said he knew a soldier who had fought at the mountain and lost his foot. He was an American Hung had chauffeured last year and was with the Number One Americans. H. drew the First Infantry Division patch believing he meant his old division.  Hung said, "Yes. Yes. They number one." H. believed that it was mostly First Division that would have any interest in Tay Ninh Province and environs now.

Throw in the 25th Infantry Division, the 173rd Airborne Brigade, assorted Special Forces and all the logistics personnel who filled out that dance card in Saigon and Bien Hoa and you'd have a party. But H. was interested again in the mountain, and an ambush site that had held a fascination and fear for him since 1966. H. loaded up at a mini-market next to the hotel on Le Loi with bottles of Evian but he felt that he should be drinking that green stuff from the canal on Ton Duc Thanh and putting chlorine tablets in it just like in the good, old days.

Near noon H. got Hung to take him to Le Caprice, a new French restaurant on the Saigon River (15th floor of the Landmark Bldg; NIKE Headquarters, Southeast Asia, among others situated in that building). This building and all those surrounding weren't even foundations in 1994. H. ate lunch looking at the Saigon River and listening to a piano player on a baby grand. $70 US, with tip—way too much for mediocre food, but the pretension was *haute*. Back at the hotel as the first monsoon storm was beginning to roll in around two pm. H. pulled back curtains to watch it. It started with a streak or two of lightening, thunder, wind blowing hard; skies darkened; VOILA; rain. It triggered big memories for H.

Later, H. found Hung and asked for a tour of the Tan Son Nhut airport area and they made a complete swing around the circumference of the airport. It was walled on all sides and off limits. This drive took well over an hour through a city that had sprung up around the airport. In the 1960's the airport was free of dwellings entirely on the north side (from map evidence anyway) and sporadically on the east and west sides. On the north side the paved road dwindled into a small laterite path almost blocked by vendors and meat and vegetable marketers selling their goods. More unhealthy and poverty-stricken living could not be found in any ghetto. They creeped along with Hung leaning on the horn for two, or three kilometers and H. got the feeling he might have to walk out because they could get no farther and there was no room to turn the car around.

Something one noted in the city was even more true in the provinces. Where one business, or artisan shop, was seen you were sure to see many more of the same category in the next several blocks as if the successful rooting of the first had spawned a host of imitators eager to profit also, duplication artists, gigantic sculpture, machinery, bicycle, antiques, all elbow to elbow, as if ghettos by artisanship had arisen.

At 4:30 pm, after successfully reconnoitering Tan Son Knut (the path flourished again into a tarmac road and finally Cach Mang Boulevard), H. walked from the Saigon Hotel to the waterfront to buy postcards. On his way he saw in one of the art reproducing shops a young man busy replicating a huge canvas, 4 ft. x 8 ft., of a famous battle scene, perhaps an El Greco. Another held up a small postcard of a Cholon street scene with French architecture and magnified it into a 3 ft. x 4 ft. canvas.

H. had scheduled Hung to take him to Long Tan, Bien Hoa, Thu Duc and Lai Thieu early the next day. H. was going to try to get ten hours of sleep to adjust his clock. Street noises picked up as skies darkened over the Saigon. From his room window H. could see welding torches in the green-netted high-rise being built two streets away as they flickered late into the night. This green netting covered all the new construction in town like cocoons. It was hung over the catwalks surrounding these new skeletons to prevent, H. guessed, debris from hurtling onto streetwalkers below. There was a man on the top floor in a shorter building to his left doing pull-ups in his underwear from a bar rigged to hold flapping laundry up to dry.

In returning from Tan Son Nhut in the afternoon, H. had Hung take him to 137 Pasteur Street which was once the site of a top-secret safe-house for Special Forces SOG operands (Studies and Observation Group; it conducted all illegal cross-border recon and other operations in Laos, Cambodia and North Vietnam). A jewelry store possessed the spot although adjacent and across the street were old French colonials (all terra cotta and stucco with mildewed walls blackened and green; original jalousies still hung from the windows) which may have been the address site in 1966. After this, H. had Hung circle the square at Notre Dame de Saigon to let him copy the inscription of the famous statue of the virgin Mary posing outside the cathedral. *Regina Pacis Oro Pro Nobis. We pray for the Queen of peace.* It was a mix and match of the secular and the holy.

H. was up the next morning as the sun started to lighten the sky. Motorbikes and traffic were beginning heavy on Ton Duc Than Boulevard paralleling the river. Some of the population were clicking small sticks already walking the streets advertising Chinese soup; Hung made the distinction for him. Chinese *Me* (Chinese soup pronounced may) versus Vietnamese *Pho* (Vietnamese soup pronounced foe). H. ate breakfast at the once notorious Brodard, on Dong Khoi Street, a block or two from the Saigon Hotel. Morning *Me* (shrimp, cauliflower, pea pods, carrots with yellow egg noodles), American coffee—more like espresso—toast and jam. It was the same restaurant Michael Herr referred to in 1966 in *Dispatches* only misspelled it:

"In Broddards and La Pagode and the pizzeria around the corner, the Cowboys and Vietnamese "students" would hang out all day, screaming obscure arguments at each other, cadging off Americans, stealing tips from the tables, reading Pleiade editions of Proust, Malraux, Camus. One of them talked to me a few times but we couldn't really communicate. All I understood was his obsessive comparison between Rome and Washington, and that he seemed to believe that Poe had been a French writer."

General Nguyen Ngoc Loan, then national commander of Vietnamese National Police and having his place in history for shooting a VC prisoner during Tet 1968, in front of Eddie Adams, whose photo became of symbol for all that was bad in the U.S./South Vietnam liaison, was reputed to have one vice; playing poker and drinking in an upstairs room over Brodard's Café. So close, yet so far away. Walking this same corridor 30 years ago H. could have looked up and saw the slender, gnomish Loan, nonfilter cigarette burning close to the fingers, ordering up another "33."

Now it was an upscale bar and restaurant in imitation of San Francisco/Chicago. Thirty years later, like Herr, Americans still couldn't communicate with anyone in this country. After the breakfast sojourn H. left with Hung for Long Tan. They took Dien Bien Phu Highway to Highway One across the Saigon River. Many new villas were being built among old shacks and the detritus of shabby factories. There was a new Coca-Cola plant 25 kilometers from Tan Son Nhut. H. took this same highway 32 years ago to the First Division base camp at Long Tan named Bearcat. The rice paddies and glades on right and left posed a mysterious danger then and H. had negotiated some of those on the left and toward Bien Hoa on foot. H. saw a small knob south of Bien Hoa, more like a rock-pile, with a pagoda perched atop, called Cho Thoi Mountain. H. decided to return to Saigon along the road that bypassed it so he could pay his respects. They crossed the Dong Nai River which bisected Bien Hoa and reached the junction of

Highway one and the route to Long Tan, and Vung Tau where the 93rd Evacuation Hospital complex was standing in 1965. Rubber trees awaited them 20 kilometers from Long Tan. There was a sign on the road translated for H. by Mr. Hung: "Drink beer and drive. Very, very, very die. Long time . . . .", and Hung crossed his hands in front of him doing his best imitation of someone in handcuffs.

They were now on the way to Bearcat. A young man was riding a motor bike with 20-30 live chickens strung off the handlebars like piñatas. There was a new BP gas station at intersection to Bearcat, but no longer any entry to Bearcat. Apparently, it had been expunged. Between the American exit from Vietnam and the end of the embargo, the Vietnamese government had loaned Bearcat (and other former American military sites) to the Russians. H. turned around and headed back to Ho Chi Minh City. In returning, H. noted that no matter where you travel in this country now, no matter how backwater, signs advertise phone numbers (and FAX numbers) and, it appearing that there was not one habitude that does not have a sign with these advertisements, every citizen in this country was selling something under an emblem. A city of thousands upon thousands of miles of storefront logos. You almost expected the population to wear phone and FAX numbers on signs hung round their necks.

When H. returned, he walked back down Dong Khoi to the river and the Majestic Hotel. This was H.'s first visit to the Majestic since he stayed in the old version in 1994. H. took the new mirrored and mahoganied elevator to the fifth-floor bar. Everything was ornate and art deco now. No geckos on the walls. Heineken beer was $3 USD. There was the same great view of the Saigon River and Ton Duc Thanh Boulevard and four Americans were at a table on the ledge, and three French at another. H. had been hearing mostly French since his return and wasn't seeing many groups of ex-G.I.s, but he noticed a lot of Japanese and Taiwanese tourists. H. walked the several blocks back to his hotel countering offers of sex, rides and drugs.

It was Saturday and H. was up at 4:40 am. He had invited Hung to breakfast at Brodard at seven am, and from there they left for the Black Virgin Mountain and Tay Ninh City. The drive to Tay Ninh City took about two and a-half hours. H. noticed now smaller replicas of the Cao Dao Temple at Tay Ninh (he saw two the day before at Di-an and near Thu Doc), something he'd missed in the 1994 trip and he didn't remember them being there in 1966-67. H. stopped to photograph one in Trang Bang, the village distinguished in history by the photo of young Vietnamese girl, Kim Phuc, running out from under a U.S. napalm attack. Now the town and roadway were full of water buffalo and cows. H. proceeded to the Black Virgin mountain and skirted Tay Ninh city driving on QL (Quon Loc) 1 on the west side and then proceeded due east on QL 13 (a road American soldiers in 1966 had called "Claymore Alley") along the southern aspect of the mountain to the new visitors parking area. It was now a full-fledged tourist mecca costing $1200 VND to enter the complex and an additional $35000 VND to ride a European style ski-gondola about half-way up the eastern face to the largest pagoda on the mountain. You had to hike the last 1000 meters to the temple on top of the mountain, if you chose. H. had hoped to take a panoramic shot of the expanse of old First Division battle grounds stretching around the mountain but had to settle for views toward Dau Tieng and Cambodia. These were good enough to compare later against the 1:50,000 maps of the 1967 Tay Ninh and estimate the exact locations of several combat and recon inserts H. had made during the War. The land appeared defoliated and watery with a tributary of the Mekong dammed up and backing water through what once had been jungle. The land was flat and shimmering all the way to Cambodia. Somewhere to the northeast was Quon Loi.

H. left the mountain about noon and headed back to Tay Ninh City to find a restaurant advertised in the Lonely Planet as the best Tay Ninh had to offer. H. hunted for it and Hung finally stopped at a pay phone and inserted a plastic credit card to call the number listed in the Lonely Travel guide for Nha Hang Diem Thuy. It was out of business. H. showed Hung the second listing (Huong Yen) and read the description of where it was; down by the river (no street address or phone number). Hung drove down to the river which looked like a sewage culvert. Hung had no idea where it was. H. asked Hung to stop and ask one of the locals where it was. Hung continued to drive and said, "Near River, No?" H. guessed Hung didn't want to go to Huong Yen, and now, neither did he. After this Hung asked several times, "You want to eat?" H. said "No. I'll save it for Ho Chi Minh City."

The afternoon rain started about noontime. It rained hard. Nobody had headlights on. When the rain was blinding you could run over somebody before you saw them. H. asked Hung if he had his on. Hung twitched his neck and nodded. That meant, "No."

The land between Tay Ninh and Ho Chi Minh City was rich with fruit and rice. The monsoon made it green and wet. Lambrettas and bicycles were overloaded with what appear to be 100-pound bags of rice (*luoa, gao, com*). Hung explained the socioeconomic divisions of rice. *Luoa* was the rice that grew in the paddy. *Gao* was the rice winnowed and bagged for market and *com* was the rice as it was served in the home and restaurant—an important distinction in a country that is the biggest consumer and exporter of rice in the world.

This countryside was richly crossed by tributaries of the Mekong River. Now in this pastoral and ancient land TV antennas protruded from mud and straw huts on bamboo and pipe flanges up through the coconut palm and banana along the roadside; between thatched roofs and clay floors, Sony and sophisticated programming. Hung said the Vietnamese love music and travel video. From the Vietnamese television H. saw back at the hotel, they also liked lecturing and parades. Perhaps the special on the tunnels of Cu Chi was in the travel category. H. guessed they were stopping in Cu Chi (town, not tunnels) so Hung could tank up on pho. He had the urge to get out of the car and ruck across the dikes and paddies for Ho Chi Minh City, just like in the halcyon days.

Returned to the road they come up on two car accidents within one kilometer of each other (about 20 kilometers from Cu Chi near the village of Go Dau). The first one involved an overloaded minibus and a Honda motorbike. The minibus was tipped sideways on the shoulder of the road with the Honda crushed under its right front wheel. The way people were crowded around the minibus and squatting and looking under the bus seemed to implicate that the Honda rider was somewhere between the right front tire, the Honda and road. Dead. The second accident had a small truck overturned on the right-hand shoulder of the road. Its chassis and wheels were facing the road and another Honda moped was flattened alongside it. A purple raincoat (empty) spread on the road next to the Honda. The rider was up an adjacent coconut tree. Dead.

H. thought about how these people drive maniacally blind in rainstorms and, BANG. Hung still hadn't turned his headlights on. Somebody told H. that the Vietnamese think that driving without the headlights saves gas. H. told Hung everybody ought to have their headlights on to warn each other in advance of the impending collision. It would give them a few seconds on the brakes and you won't end so far up in the coconut tree. Hung twitched his neck and nodded. Hung, old-hand that he was, knew better and drove on blindly into the storm, saving gas.

Somewhat past Go Dau, ducks were corralled in a quadrangle of rice paddy dikes like cattle. Duck farming. The rain was coming down hard. The paddies on both sides of the road were being worked by bending women clearing, planting, reaping? They looked like Millet's Reapers. There were stalls of rice paper vendors along the road before Bien Hoa. Millions of sheets, mostly in ovals and all sizes. In the distance a young girl came out from a house with a terra cotta roof and walked along a dike. She was dressed in a pastel orange shirt. There was a coffin vendor on the right with about 20 new cement coffins, or maybe synthetic material; brick makers and kilns all along the road.

H. wanted to see the temple on top of Cho The Mountain, so Hung proceeded across the Dong Nai after driving through Bien Hoa. Bien Hoa. He did't even take a second look, but in 1966, he thought it was an epiphany for Vietnam:

"Sampans bobbing on the oilslicked waters fronting the busy verandah of the Hotel ______ on Kim Lun Street. The heavy water of the Dong Nai lapping at the rusted metals of converted gunboats, landing craft, diesel junks, river steamers and tethered barges. Kim Lun Street blending steamy tarmac with the terres rouge of Kratie; klaxon clang and jingle of lambrettas, cyclos, mopeds and iron-hulled tricars singing with the throaty horns of Renault, Peugeot, Citroen and diesel spewing Mercedes. The shops and market tables displaying fresh loaves, ripe fruit, wet trays of abalone, shark fin, crab, coralpinkshrimp, glassblackseaslugs. Vendors cooking in open wares boiling congees of bean and lemon with glasine noodles. Old women with gnarled redstained fingers wrapping meat paste cakes and sticky rice cake in banana leaves and barking their goods by spangled shops of cloth and crystal and bronze.

Cloudy waters gathering in remnant benzoin staved barrels beneath awnings and eaves of decorated canvas and bamboo. A vermilion song of commerce—the pimp and merchant, bonze and soldier—assailing the city's perfumes of rotted fruit, excrement and fermentation. Rattan, palmyra, blossoming sago and white narcissus decking the jutting verandah of the Hotel ______. White-jacketed waiters proceeding drafts of clove and tangerine, jasmine, pepper sauce and coriander in advance escort of steaming trays of choice repast; tom vo vien, bisque du Homard, sates, Kan-pei in butyric slush of putrid fish.

The morning air is scented by a dark burst of rain, rests warmly in the narrow passageways and streets of Bien Hoa and moves in a palpable mist on the beetled waters of the green Dong Nai toward the tussock, bamboo and pilang waving at the edge of a far shore."

Kim Lun Street was fictional but H.'s interest over the intervening years turned toward the south shore of the Dong Nai, beyond the tussock, bamboo and pilang waving at the edge, and the twenty miles or more south to Saigon.

H. reach the temple at Cho Thoi Mountain at about noon and climbed old slab and cement stairways some 500 meters to the pagoda. It was not situated on the top but was perched to the southern side about three-quarters of the way up. Children and beggars confronted him on his ascent. H. stopped and took a piss in long grass half-way up the incline. Beggars were squatting a little higher up. H. donated $10000 VND, sweating and breathing hard at the top. A family with several girls and boys took turns taking and posing for his photos. Nothing spectacular, but a good view of rock quarry below, but the north side of the mountain hides the pagoda from any northern view of Bien Hoa. H. could not see the Hotel on Kim Lun Street, or the bamboo, tussock and pilang on the Dong Nai. H. could see Hung far below waiting in the car for his return, impatient for pho. The pagoda and its statuary were scaffolded and apparently under a tourist upscale.

H. turned to Di-an, once the Headquarters of the U.S. First Infantry Division, and encountered small rain showers and large, gray clouds over Saigon. H. asked Hung to head west to Phu Cuong, ever so discreetly, ever so secretly. Phu Cuong was the real reason behind H.'s return to Vietnam in 1994, but he could not work up the courage after an ominous coincidence that involved Nhu Tran, his driver that year. Nhu Tran said he was going out to the construction site of the home he was finally building in Vietnam. When H. asked Tran where, Tran said, Lai Thieu. Lai Thieu was the seat of Phu Cuong geography. Surprised by that revelation H. could no longer broach the facts of his wish to visit Phu Cuong to Tran, imagining that perhaps this was Tran's birth land and he knew of the ambush, or worse had family, or friends killed in it. It was paranoia of a festering type, growing as one took the time to make up new explanations.

H. had marked the location down to meters on his map for this odyssey and intended to see it this time, come hell, or high water. The ambush happened October 27, 1966, and had involved about 25 women and children going to market place at four in the morning. It would have been an atrocity if it had been willful, but it was accidental. The incident took place about four kilometers south of Phu Cuong (Lai Thieu Province) near a graveyard and a pagoda.

The area was already famous for a combat action that occurred almost exactly one year earlier (October 22, 1965) when Company B, 2nd Battalion, 503rd Infantry of the 173rd Airborne Brigade came under attack by a large Viet Cong force at Phu Cuong. In the ensuing fight, a grenade landed in the middle of one platoon. PFC Milton Olive, "in the time it takes for a bullet to travel 900 meters, or a toad's tongue to snatch a fly, or a person to hiccup . . .

knew exactly what he was going to do, what he needed to do."[29] He grabbed the grenade and pulled it into his chest hugging it. It exploded and Olive absorbed the full force of the blast. Several of his comrades were wounded but all survived while Olive died instantly. For that sacrifice, Olive became the first African-American awarded the Medal of Honor in Vietnam. In 1966, nobody told the 16th Infantry Rangers about their predecessors—Milton Olive and the 173rd Airborne Brigade.

So, it is to this place, apparently a ground of tragedy far before October 27, 1966, that Hung carried H. They turned right on Highway 13 at Phu Cuong. H. showed Hung the map with the ambush site marked. At about four kilometers he looked for a road junction on the right, and found it. The names in the area didn't correspond to those on the 1967 map, but there was no doubting that this was the area of the ambush. They proceeded down the secondary road about half a kilometer and saw the graveyard on the right. Just as they came up on the cemetery the skies blackened like Golgotha at the crucifixion and the

---

[29] Zullo, Allan, *10 True Tales: Vietnam War Heroes,* 2014, p. 42.

rains poured down in torrents (H. photographed the graveyard and rainstorm). Ominous? No. It was another afternoon of monsoon. The midday rains. Here H. was within spitting distance of October 27, 1966, but to look at the country and the countryside, he might as well have been on the moon—the dark side.

WAR & REMEMBRANCE

BACK TO VIETNAM: A SOLDIER'S STORY ON THE 20TH ANNIVERSARY OF THE FALL, *STYLE WEEKLY,* April 18, 1995, Richmond, Virginia

It's the dead of the night and I am returning to Vietnam after a 27 year hiatus. Ho Chi Minh City—still Saigon to its inhabitants—is lit up 100,000 Chinese lantern-watts as we drop under the cloud cover and approach Tan Son Nhut Airport. Even at midnight, I can make out the shapes of aging American transport planes rusted to the runway. Helicopters stand rotorless. Two or three less-than-virgin white Boeing airbuses, recently leased from France, are parked and empty on the concourse.

I have come to see a mountain that has loomed large in my memory. Veterans from all over our country are returning to Vietnam. Some go in hope of healing a psyche wound. I have come back because war, in a young man's mind, makes an indelible impression, and this war and this country are indelibly in my memory. I'm returning to see Vietnam again, and to see if it has changed.

Tay Ninh was a noticeable place long before the war if for nothing more than the cathedral that resembled a Disney fantasy and marked the seat of the Cao-Dai religion in Tay Ninh City. A British travel writer said in the 50s that from a distance it appeared to be the monstrous result of marriage between a pagoda and a southern baroque church but at close range was the most outrageously vulgar building ever to have been erected with serious intent.

The Cao-Dai faith is a 20th century invention, a phenomenon of eclecticism counting among its hierarchy of Saints Victor Hugo, Winston Churchill, Lao-Tse, Buddha and Jesus Christ. Worship takes place between pink endragoned pillars and church iconography where the male Pope has female Cardinals and makes prophecy from a ouija board.

But it was because of the mountain that the temple was built and the Black Virgin Mountain, or Nui Ba-Den, is a sight to behold:

". . . a single symmetrical mountain humps up suddenly from the plain, rising from what must be practically sea-level to 3000 feet. As there is not another hillock for fifty miles in any direction to break the flat and featureless monotony of Cochin-China, this darkly forested plumpudding silhouette is quite remarkable. In a part of the world where every religion has its sacred mountain, such an eminence is obviously irresistible. Consequently, it has been since dimmest antiquity a place of revelation. Its slopes are said to be riddled with caves, both natural and artificial, housing at one time or other the cult objects of numerous sects." (Norman Lewis in *A Dragon Apparent*; the British travel writer referred to above).

I drive up Highway 22 and through a nondescript village, Trang Bang, where 20 years ago a heartbreaking scene played out when a young girl named Kim Phuc ran out from under a napalm attack screaming and shedding her burning cloths naked to the camera. It is not far past Trang Bang I see Nui Ba-Den for the first time since 1967. It is a hazy, green bowler hat rising above a treeline southwest of Tay Ninh City.

In November 1966, with the beginning of Operation Attleboro, we flew in low over this same treeline coming into full view of the Black Virgin before landing in a basecamp named Dau Tieng. Attleboro, or the Battle of Dao Tieng, was a fight waged in classic proportions enlisting elements of the 5th Special Forces Group, 25th Infantry Division, 196th Light Infantry Brigade and the First Infantry Division.

At the beginning of this operation an unlikely and ominous event occurred as a command helicopter from the 1st Battalion 28th Infantry (First Infantry Division) was lifting out of Dau Tieng. Losing power, it ran head on into a Catholic Church steeple posed like a sentinel at the head of the runway and crashed and burned killing nine of the 11 men on board. This same battalion was assaulted two days later between dark and dawn in a landing zone too small for a battalion with company lines stretching into the entangling forest.

The Viet Cong attacking force, heavily decimated by U.S. artillery and air attacks after the first assault, regathered and with a screaming of horns and whistles made a final headlong charge on the 28th. A line of claymores stopped the attack dead. At 0900 hours a 28th Infantry gunner ended enemy contact by blistering the upper reaches of a mahogany tree, tumbling an enemy sniper still clutching a Browning automatic rifle to the ground. The bullet stream had severed the rope the sniper used to tie himself in to the tree.

At 1000 hours my unit, 2nd Battalion 16th Infantry Rangers, was beginning descent into a landing zone some five kilometers south of the 28th Infantry action. I remember watching the orange-plumed clusters of high explosive walking in measured step through the towering jungle canopy; ordnance shot from heavy guns poised around that same church steeple. What I recall most vividly, however, was movement high in the wall of trees as the rumbling helicopters dropped under treetop level making a final, mad dash to the region of *foret-clairiere* opening like a mineshaft below. The movement, large and shackled, had been that of a VC soldier roped in to a tree in fatal prospicience.

In that landing zone, called JOE, we were subjected immediately to intense small arms and automatic weapons fire from the 271st VC Regiment entrenched in bunkers. I found myself, when the initial action was ceased, in front of enemy bunkers so well hidden that only muzzle flash revealed their locations. The 16th lost two men with 14 wounded. The 28th lost 28 men and

42 were wounded. Based on the size of the VC force and the heavy artillery and air strikes, there may well have been 400 or more young conscripts from Hanoi and environs lost forever on that day in that dark and foreboding forest, all within view of the Black Virgin Mountain.

Four months later, during the largest ground operation ever conducted in the war, Operation Junction City, I flew into a field designated LZ GEORGE covered with tall meadow-like grass surrounded by medium to heavy jungle. The previous day and night two battalions of the First Infantry Division had survived the assault of three battalions of the 271st VC Regiment (our nemesis in November) and elements of the 70th Guard Regiment. The battle included horn-blowing human wave assaults, hand-to-hand combat and massive air and artillery strikes. After the fight, called the Battle of Ap Gu, strings of enemy dead were found where cluster bomb runs had literally curled them up 10 meters from U.S. perimeters. LZ GEORGE was littered with enemy dead and body counts totaled upward of 600. The 16th moved through the fields of enemy dead followed by Rome plows. The plows carved huge scars across GEORGE to hide in shallow graves another cross-section of Vietnam's finest beneath the shadow of the Black Virgin Mountain.

It has been estimated that these pitched battles baiting VC and NVA forces into large unit confrontations to face annihilation under heavy U.S. artillery and air strikes killed hundreds of thousands of the enemy. Most had the ignominious epitaph and gravesite described above. I cannot help thinking that they are as missing in action as any American who never readventured from this land.

As I come to this monument of a mountain now bared by herbicide defoliations in the war, and up close so shrunken and unimpressive, I am keenly aware of being surrounded by a people who have suffered terrible losses. In this place some 300,000 sisters, sons, mothers, fathers, loved ones dot the countryside in mass graves. There are far more than 2000 missing in action on this plain. It is hard to feel the injured party in front of this mountain.

The Black Virgin Mountain is crowded by vehicles and throngs of people at its base for the moon is full on this day and acolytes have come from afar in Vietnam to worship at the relics housed in and on the mountain. I am disturbed by the heat, the dryness and these memories and turn back to Tay Ninh City to take in another religious spectacle, this one housed in the cool marble and tile of the most outrageously vulgar building ever to have been erected with serious intent.

* * * * * *

It was an unexpected beauty at the end of an ugly piece of road. Quon Loi was northwest of Saigon and stood on the Ho Chi Minh Trail as it entered South Vietnam from Cambodia. It was once a swarming center of rubber production and processing for the latex of Michelin rubber plantation and perched on a rubber treed antipode four kilometers east of An Loc, a name made famous in 1972 when the NVA began a final assault on South Vietnam and Saigon.

In Saigon I hire an interpreter and his shockless Honda on Dong Khoi Street to trace a path back to this oasis in the western corner of Binh Long province. The Quon Loi I remember was distinguished by large French manor homes built about a 1500-meter airstrip. A pavilion with Olympic swimming pool and one and three-meter diving boards punctuated the southwest end; a nine-hole golf course bordered the northeast stretching between terra cotta roofed houses dotting a tussocky hillside sloping down to a marsh valley below. An old Vietnamese gentleman and his beautiful, dark-haired daughter ran a laundry and market. The airstrip was set between towering rubber that seemed to announce, "This is a haven."

I am dummied up now making this drive up Highway 13, once known as "Claymore Alley"; like an Oklahoma farmer parsing the route General Lee took from Chancellorsville to Appomattox. Can't quite grasp the past because the present keeps warping the portend. In Appomattox it's Burger King. Here it's all those 1990 Hondas.

It is March 1994. March is the Sahara of Vietnam. It has not rained during the two weeks I've been in country and monsoon is still a good two months away. This is fine for travelers, but bad for aesthetes: monsoon makes an Eden out of this country.

Perhaps because of the dryness I don't recognize An Loc as we drive up the gently rising highway that circles into this former rubber baron of Indochina. I look for an apothecary I remember as prominent at the juncture of Highway 13 and provincial route 303 leading uphill and eastward to Quon Loi, but the few buildings that seem original are heavily pockmarked from exploded ordnance. As I leave An Loc, the rubble of battles waged in this once handsome, but innocuous town amidst rubber trees seems to stand it in a time capsule.

So shockless sedan and passengers wend their way the final kilometers to the mystery plateau to arrive atop a fingered peninsula of land jutting northeast into a valley of marshland and what may once have been dense forest and jungle. But this plateau is an expanse of nakedness overgrown with dried gorse and weeds. There are no columns of old-growth rubber stretching more than a mile down a glistening runway. There are no manor houses, no palatial club with amenities, no laundry and market. It is dry. One spark would set this tinder box raging to Saigon.

I begin walking through brushwood toward the northeastern end of the hill. The interpreter calls, "Here. Here is the airfield." Where a new laterite rutted road has been worn by cart and car, remnant tarmac appears in jigsaw pieces. The laterite road is cut from the southwest to the northeast just as the once busy runway had aligned itself and in walking the mile or so length of it I trace clots of broken tarmac in the maze of gorse and laterite.

So, I stand in the middle of this land and turn slowly and try to authenticate the feeling I have carried all these years that this spot a world away from my home was a signal place. I think that if I close my eyes I will hear the scream of helicopter turbines as they begin to turn black rotors, the murmur of jeeps and one-quarter ton trucks and the patter of raindrops on broad rubber leaves.

Somewhere, from the tall stand of rubber, young voices will rise, attempting to harmonize the Beach Boys 'Sloop John B. And if I open my eyes time will reverse itself and I will stand once again between the towering rubber of Quon Loi, broad leaves still slick and resonant with night's rainfall as the mists of war run out across the waving green jungle to Cambodia.

But it is not to be. A generation has already passed from this land and the earth that abideth here does not seem to be the land that rose to meet me when I was young and eager and in expectation of so much less.

* * * * * *

On several of my last mornings in Vietnam I have noticed a tall Asian in the lobby of the

Majestic hotel where I am lodging. He is an elegant figure, 50ish, dressed like an American CEO on vacation from the Eisenhower administration. I peg him from Taiwan. One morning, after the usual nod and "How's it going?" he asks me:

"Where are you from?"

"The USA. Virginia."

"Ah, yes. I am from California. San Jose."

"Why are you in Vietnam?"

"Vietnam is my home. I am from Vietnam. In Virginia, where are you from?"

"Richmond."

"Ah, yes. Richmond. You know Arlington, Virginia?"

"Yes. Arlington. Little Saigon, Wilson Boulevard."

"Ah, yes. I know. I have good friend in Arlington. You know him. He very famous. On cover of TIME magazine. Very famous. Shoot VC in head."

"General Loan?"

"Yes. General Nguyen Ngoc Loan. He is my good friend."

In saying this he has confirmed one of my observations from this trip about the relationship of old enemies and the new Vietnamese Republic. The Vietnamese treat tragedy like Brughel's

Icarus. Do you recall W.H. Auden's *Musee des Beaux Arts*, so full of angst and forgetfulness? Tragedy takes place while someone else is eating or opening a window:

In Brughel's Icarus for instance: how everything turns away
Quite leisurely from the disaster; the ploughman may
Have heard the splash, the forsaken cry,
But for him it was not an important failure; the sun shone
As it had to on the white legs disappearing in the green
Water; and the expensive delicate ship that must have seen
Something amazing, a boy falling out of the sky
Had somewhere to get to and sailed calmly on.

The photo my elegant friend spoke of didn't debut on the cover of *Time*. It appeared five columns wide and five inches deep on the cover of the February 2, 1968 *New York Times*, and showed an image caught by Eddie Adams during the madness of the 1968 Tet Offensive. General Nguyen Ngoc Loan has, revolver pointed at the head of a Viet Cong suspect, pulled the trigger splattering a fearsome picture into world memory. But there is more to the photo than tragedy. There are so many things turned leisurely from the disaster.

On a street corner near An Quang Pagoda, Chinese lanterns bedeck a hanging lamp wire in sienna above the areca leaves stretching down the street running from the lower left-hand corner; the afternoon light is caught against the washed lemon of the French balconies with green-shuttered windows and the potted ivy that begins a swirling descent to the balcony above the painted sign for *Jollier Diamantaire*. The sun shining through shading tamarinds belies the horror rooted firmly down the street and at the center of the photo. I have returned to Vietnam, remembered something amazing and, now, having somewhere to get to, will go calmly on my way.

THE TRIPLE-CANOPIED JUNGLE

A REVIEW OF
Dispatches
Michael Herr
Avon, 1984. 274 pages. Paper, $3.95
Cloth (Knopf, 1978) is out of print

But somewhere all the mythic tracks intersected, from the lowest John Wayne wetdream to the most aggravated soldier-poet fantasy, and where they did I believe that everyone knew everything about everyone else, every one of us there a true volunteer.

– Michael Herr, *Dispatches*

Soldier-poet fantasies. Recently, in leafing through S.L.A. Marshall's *Ambush*, a compilation of battle narratives treating an American Infantry operation (Operation Attleboro) in Vietnam in the fall of 1966, I noticed continuous references to the First Infantry Division. I served with the First Division (2nd Bn/16th Infantry Rangers) during this period and was curious to find, perhaps, a familiar face, recognizable geography.

I discovered a battle had ended where one of ours had begun, only notable because of a coincidence of war. On November 6, at about 0600 hours, in a broad reticulation of abandoned paddy fields surrounded by secondary jungle with double-canopied top, the 1st/28th Infantry of the First Infantry Division came under encircling fire and attack from a large NAVA force. In a firefight lasting four hours the 28th Infantry suffered heavy casualties. S.L.A. Marshall's narrative closes with a 28th machine-gunner blistering the upper reaches of a mahogany, tumbling an enemy sniper, still clutching a BAR (Browning Automatic Rifle) to the ground. The bullet stream had severed the rope the sniper had used to tie himself into the tree.

At 1000 hours, November 6, the 2nd/16th was beginning descent into a landing zone some ten kilometers south of the 28th Infantry action. I remember watching the orange-plumed clusters of high explosive walking in measured step through the towering canopy; ordnance shot from heavy guns poised round a church steeple in far off Dau Tieng. What I recall most vividly, however, was movement high in the wall of trees as the rumbling helicopters dropped under tree-top level making a final mad dash to the region of *forêt-clairière* opening like a mineshaft below. The movement, large and shackled, had been that of a North Vietnamese soldier roped in to a tree in fatal prospicience.

Dispatches is a triple-canopied jungle where the enemy constantly lurks tied into teak and ebenaceae; where the war is as much the stentor of helicopters as the ride in; where premonition and coincidence are more important than intelligence reports, lessons learned and leadership. One reads these pages and begins to doubt his own experience in Vietnam, or refits his personal memory to the real and surreal contours of this myth-fascinated poet who, in describing his place in the war said, "I was there to watch." In saying so he begins unraveling a central paradox of war, one as common to the soldier as the correspondent; the problem of ambivalence. *Dispatches* is nothing if not a chronicle of irresolution and more mightily so because of Herr's position as a watcher, even "voyeur" (as he develops it). But it is a special kind of vacillation, for Herr manages, in the end, to stride the chasm between observation and participation. He becomes, with an urge as contradictory as the war, a true volunteer. It is the documentation of this paradox which separates Herr's book from most of what has been, and is being, written about Vietnam.

What has been, and is being, written about Vietnam takes up large space. In this year of decennial commemoration it is reported that twelve new books are published on Vietnam each month. The *Vietnam War Bibliography* (Christopher L. Sugnet and John L. Hickey) has 3003 entries chosen from an initial selection of over 7000 titles, and includes analyses, historical treatments, personal narratives, pamphlets, manuscript documents, archival materials and fiction; these in English, Vietnamese, French and other Western languages and Indonesian. One requires a taxonomy to divide the subjects and interests of the Vietnam War.

Herr's writing does not open a new genre. The style and intent belong to that school of journalistic innovation attributed to Truman Capote's venture in the nonfiction novel (*In Cold Blood*) some 20 years previous and imitated, synthesized, or magnified by the likes of Hunter S. Thompson, Tom Wolfe, Norman Mailer and

Shana Alexander since. A closer inspection might trace the original of this style to James Boswell's *Life of Johnson* which makes a case for biography, autobiography fiction and the r*oman à clef*.

Herr has taken the genre to war and that is something not accomplished before. He has also made out of his own experience in Vietnam an apostate portrait. Apostatic because he seems to have forsaken reason in his decision to relinquish the relative safety of journalism in Saigon for the fear and loathing of the real war; portrait, because his works are a canvas from which Vietnam, in secret and soniselectric technicolor, is raised in black lumps of tomentosa and fronds as the artist poses.

Mr. Herr says, and it has become a blurb, "I think that Vietnam was what we had instead of happy childhoods." Another aspect of the paradox of ambiguity? We see these ironies—terror/happiness, beauty/ghastliness and love/hate—developed over and over again in a counterpoint of sensible melody amid the dissonant voices of Vietnam. Voices are sorted out, and the shit from the shinola:

"Hearts and Minds, Peoples of the Republic, tumbling dominoes, maintaining the equilibrium of the Ding-dong by containing the ever encroaching Doodah; you could also hear the other, some young soldier speaking in all bloody innocence, saying, 'All that's just a load, man. We're here to kill gooks. Period.'"

Herr's discussions of identity and irony, further, focus on the position of the correspondent and the perceived differences between observation and action (spell action with a capital A). If there is a central theme in this book it is one which speaks to something, we, as young infantry soldiers, described in Vietnam (and ever after) as the rear echelon m_____ f_____, or REMF. You were either in the rear, or you were a warrior, although one came to understand, with study and perseverance, that there existed so many divisions of the rear, and all the space leading to the mytho-mystical front, that use of the word implied some form of discrimination. It did not when war was war, when, as Jeremiah Denton was heard to say, "Hell was in session."

Herr was concerned with this hierarchy of service during his three years in the country, for he did not want to be identified with that *lumpen* gender of correspondents (some 700 strong during the Ten Offensive) which included feature writers for religious organs, gun magazines, summer vacationers from college newspapers, second-string hacks and syndicated eminences who spent the war sipping calvados at the *Cercle Sportif* more enamored of the morning line at the Phu Tho horse track than the war that had brought them in the first place. Many writers and correspondents in Vietnam, simply put, had come to see the razzmatazz and grab a "quick feel" of the war.

Herr's aversion to the quick feel is outlined in a rite of passage that is far more interesting than those journals of growth which follow the young Marine, or Soldier, through basic training, advanced training, a baptism by fire and the long journey home. When Herr writes about Lurps (LRRPS), Seals, Recondos, Green Beret bushmasters, redundant mutilators, heavy rapers, eye-shooters, widow-makers, nametakers, point men, *isolatos,* outriders and soldiers with eyes that made you feel like you were being watched from hundreds of hidden caves, he speaks about a side of the war he lived.

He needed the horror show to define himself. His rite of passage is a portrait of the correspondent as rifleman. He walked on patrols near the savage rim of Cambodia, through the entangling lianas of Tay Ninh, down long aisles of shading hevea in the Michelin. He kissed Vietnamese soil, ate it, plowed it, sat asswards to .50-caliber fire at 2000 feet while watching a young Marine across from him go into a dying whiplash and fired cover in Can Tho with a .30-caliber automatic for a four-man reaction team trying to get back through the wire.

He does not do it alone. There are kindred souls, colleagues who, by some coincident pathology, must also have the war and hate it too. One can make out a quadrille of sensibility and style. Sean Flynn, son of the late swashbuckler Errol Flynn, was a first-rate combat photographer who would go anywhere to get the picture and finally went into the maw of Cambodia never to return. Dana Stone, leathered New Englander and consummate combat photographer, went anywhere, went to Cambodia with Flynn, did not return. Tim Page, London orphan, *bon vivant*, combat photographer, and wounded once for every correspondent in Vietnam. A fraternity of ambivalents:

"We were called thrill freaks, death wishers, wound seekers, war lovers, hero-worshippers, closet queens, dope addicts, low-grade alcoholics, ghouls, communist seditionists, more nasty things than I can remember. There were people in the military who never forgave General Westmoreland for not imposing restrictions against us when he'd had the chance in the early days."

All possessors of the right stuff, for that is what they had, what they admired in the professionals, the unwilling grunts, the amateurs with a penchant. Their tale, full of sound and fury, is not told by an idiot. Herr transports the history and literature of this war in map pockets and alice-pack and refers to them often with diacritical accuracy. It is what you'd expect from one who notices Vietnamese students in Brodards and La Pagode reading *Pléiade* editions of Proust, Malraux, Camus. Joseph Conrad's Kurz and Lord Jim are reference points for the odd spook living out some strange advisory stint in the middle of Laos ("You didn't see a thing, right Chief. You weren't even here."). Graham Greene had it right in *The Quiet American*:

"Maybe it was already over for us in Indochina when Alden Pyle's body washed up under the bridge a Dakao, his lungs all full of mud; maybe it caved in with Dien Bien Phu. But the first happened in a novel, and while the second happened on the ground, it happened to the French, and Washington gave it no more substance than if Graham Greene had made it up too."

Dispatches is not simple journalism. All this talk about ambiguity, death wishes, war-heroes, and the rear tends to obscure the significance of the writing. Herr introduced a language in this book that will serve as a dialectic for future aficionados of the Vietnam War. The cadences and accents combine in a portmanteau of rock and roll, technotrash and *horrida bella* to report war like it's never been reported before. Vietnam becomes a living, breathing malignancy; a menace of flora and fauna. Michael Herr's prose and his dictions are the heavy artillery recalling Vietnam for all of us, one way or another.

Part Two
FICTIONS

SAIGON PASSIONAL

Then to the third-a face nor child nor old, very calm, as of
Beautiful yellow-white ivory;
Young man I think I know you-I think this face is the face
Of the Christ himself,
Dead and divine and brother of all, and here again he lies.

—Walt Whitman, *A Sight In Camp In the Daybreak Gray and Dim*

An actually existent fly is more important than a possible existent angel.

—Ralph Waldo Emerson

The United States Army Mortuary was encompassed by a slat and beam fence and housed in the sprawling Personnel Property Depot, USA Support Command, Saigon, erected by Raymond International & Morrison-Knudsen. It stood at the southeast end of Tan Son Knut Airport and away from the larger MACV Annex. The mortuary was built of wood and corrugated tin finished in Arctic green and double thick insulation with a gray ventilation weasand running the length of the roof. Rising above eaves level, hooded air-conditioning vents poked from ducts like the communication funnels of a large merchant ship.

Entering the Mortuary at Area A from the 80 percent humidity of Saigon, Myrtle Jones was burnt by a freezing wind. Area A was a refrigeration unit cooling more than a hundred bodies awaiting transportation back to the U.S. She walked from the refrigeration unit into the embalming chamber scattered with ten embalming tables then entered the abdomen of the building; an atrium of wall shelves holding newly embalmed bodies on general support litters. The bodies glowed from a sheen of hexaphene MA37 recently applied in preserving cocoons. The graveyard shift had all but disappeared to morning chow and the bunk.

She entered the WDMET area where wounds data on munitions effectiveness was collected and saw the body on the solitary pathology table in the center of the room. A calendar featuring Bireley's orange pop, *A Drink For Good Health and New Vitality*, was pinned to the far wall. The odor of hexaphene and formaldehyde cloyed.

Picking up and reading from a collection of field reports, eyewitness statements, and operation records in an ochre file folder, Myrtle saw that the body on the porcelain pathology table belonged to the former Cooper comma Felix A period comma Sergeant. A Caribou had flown the body from the mortuary collection point at Quon Loi on the Cambodian border. Three hours earlier, under the cover of darkness, the plane had taxied down one of the northeast runways of Tan Son Knut barely a thousand meters from the entrance to the mortuary off Quang Trung Road. Myrtle looked at the face of the Seiko watch on her left wrist. The hands showed 0845 hrs.

An olive drab body bag with one carrying handle exposed was unzipped, folded back on the floor and propped against a duraluminum leg of the mortuary table. It looked like the abused leaf of a giant Moses-In-The-Cradle plant; dark green on the topside, dark purple on the underside. A large piece of masking tape marked–

HOLD FOR POST

hung from the zipper closure. The chilled room was redolent with the sweet, nasty smell of brackish waters of the Saigon River pushed in by opening and closing doors shunting cooled air out.

Myrtle looked momentarily to the east window where the river, unseen for the seven-foot slat fence, meandered a scant distance away in its sluggish progress northward to Bien Hoa. Mortuary supplies and equipment lined the east wall of the WDMET area in metal-shelved inventory; 15 gallon drums of embalming fluid (cavity and arterial), dermasurgery wax in one pound cans, gooseneck embalming tubes (brass and steel), hardening compound in five gallon metal pails, injector and embalming needles, trocars of varying lengths, replacement mortuary head rests of molded semi-hard rubber fabrication and an electric portable sealer. A vertical mirror measuring three by six feet with wood veneer frame was fastened by punched tin brackets to a shelf post of the supply case directly across from the pathology table.

Myrtle walked to it and standing on her toe tips reached to the top shelf to turn on a small, brown radio dialed to 99.9 FM, Armed Forces Radio Vietnam. She looked at her reflection in the mirror luminous on the edges from the ceiling arc of a 1000-watt, floodlight Gerry rigged above the table. Staring back at her were sad, luminous, blue eyes some drunken sailor once told her made her look like Yvette Mimieux. She lifted her right hand to her short auburn hair running her plain-nailed fingers gently from front to back returning with middle finger to her lips. She wiped with downward pull a discernment of sun-shimmering shade of Max Factor UltraLucent Crème Iridescent lipstick in California Coral from the left corner of her mouth.

She turned ten degrees to her left and lifted the right heel of her Panama-soled tropical boot posing her right knee in front of her left, her hands bunning her hair up from the back of her neck. The cotton, herringbone twill field shirt and cotton, sateen carded slacks hid in starched creases and pockets the curves of her hips and breasts. Her short hair corresponded with a regulation that required it be neat and well-groomed yet not extend below the bottom edge of the collar nor be cut so short as to present an unfeminine appearance. She had never had to worry about an unfeminine appearance. Soldiers told her she was too pretty to be in the Women's Army Corps. They apparently thought this was some kind of compliment but Myrtle always heard it as a criticism.

The corpse materialized under her absent gaze. She saw that it had already begun swelling, characteristic of the decomposition occurring so quickly with too long exposure to the noonday sun in Vietnam—already the surprising odor of rot.

Myrtle took from an open brown wrapper on a trundle cabinet a blue surgical smock off a pile of autoclaved smocks and pulled its three-holed bag over her head covering her fatigues to midthigh. She turned from these preparations and made her first observation of the corpse. *DD 891, Record of Identification-Dental Chart*, positively identified Sergeant Cooper. Attached to the right wrist was a paper and wire tag reading in part,

MACV-SOG, 5TH SFG.
LOCATION—CLASSIFIED/TOP SECRET

The thumb and fingers were oddly contracted into the palm and a blood-caked wound covered most of the wrist above the palm. Turning the hand Myrtle could see the same wound on the posterior wrist. A glance at the left wrist revealed an identical wound, identical crabbing of the hands. The bones of the feet and ankles protruded from below the ruined and macerated flesh of the legs. The tibia and fibula of the left leg were exposed, as were parts of the femur up to the symphysis pubis face of the pubis and unavoidably at the center of this path, instead of a penis, a ripped and dark vesicle of flesh.

Myrtle still did not look into the face of the dead soldier. It remained clouded in the periphery of her vision as she kept her eyes on the wreckage of the young body resting with clinched palms ceilingward and inswept. She observed that the acronyms, secrecy, and terrible wounds had something to do with the US Army Green Berets, for with the remains was a tightly rolled green felt trademark, which when opened revealed a shield of orange, black, and white with a metal crest of arrows crossed upon a sword surrounded by a scroll inscribed in Latin, *De Oppresso Liber*. She began to sing softly and hum where she did not know the words a stanza from a ballad that had reached the top of American pop music charts three months earlier:

Fighting soldiers from the sky,
Those brave men who jump and die.
Duh-duh-duh-daaaa, Duh-duh-duh-day,
But only three wear the Green Beret.

It was rumored that the composer, a Green Beret sergeant, had written it in a whorehouse in Mexico.

The address for the effects inventory was Thu Duc, 5th Special Forces Group (ABN). The records revealed that Cooper had been a member of a six-man recon team, otherwise unidentified, found in a spot on the Cambodian-Vietnam border and near a geographic location given on the map as Bao Menk. The remnant uniform attached to the remains was a camouflage ERDL stripped of unit signifiers and personal identification. Turning away from the face of the corpse, Myrtle began to read from the *Report of Recovery Activities*:

> Remains found at 1845 hours 18 August 1966, at XT 872666, Map Sheet 6332-III, AMS Vietnam 1:50,000, were recovered in two hours. Search party included elements of the 1st Inf Div, 2nd Bde, located at Quon Loi. Remains found nailed through the hands to a mangrove stump in approx. 3-4 ft. of water. Remains mutilated with gunshot wounds, impalement wounds and environmental damage. Nails were not recovered.

She flipped further to the *DA Form 2773-R* searching for the circumstances of death:

> Circumstances: Recon Team in area XT 872666, Dong Menk Key, 3 kilometers due south Srok Chala on Quan An Loc, Quan Loc Ninh border; nipa and mangrove swamp located between elevations NW and SE of the Tonle Trou river.

Page two noted other personnel killed in the action:

> *SSG FRYE, William R.TSN 2467-66*
> *SGT DuTremble, RobertTSN 2468-66*
> *Nguyen Ai Quoc, Trung Si* ___________
> *Lui Van Toom, Trung Si*___________
> *Boun Blech, Ha Si*___________

The circumstances of death were not given for the other members of the patrol. She read on. The weaponry list on *DD 890* caught her eye:

Recovered:
1 K-Bar Knife, 7 1/2"; 2 rifle magazines (empty).

> Unrecovered:
> 3 Swedish K submachine guns, 9mm M-45; 2 XM177ESZ submachine guns; 1 sawed-off Ithaca 12-gauge pump shot gun w/24 rounds

> 00 buckshot; 10 'flechette 'rounds, Browning high power; 6 claymores; 8 las. C-4 plastic; 18 M61A frag grenades; 6 M59 concussion grenades; 6 M34 WP grenades; 5 K-Bar knives, 7 1/2"; 114 rifle magazines.

Myrtle pulled from the file a rag of paper torn page-size with tattered edges from the grid squares of an artillery map. The map-side was stained through. The reverse was hand-printed semi-legibly in what appeared to be blood:

> *WE GET BACK*
> *YOUR X RAY*
> *& THINK WE*
> *KNOW PROBLEM*

The map note had a slash hole through the words X RAY and THINK. Myrtle shuffled to *DA 10-249, Certificate of Death*. In addition to the several primary traumatic causes given for death the form listed under <u>Other Significant Conditions</u> a further explanation:

> KIA had note fashioned from patrol map fragment reading WE

GET BACK YOUR X RAY AND THINK WE KNOW PROBLEM impaled in chest at sternum with a knife having a 7 1/2" blade.

She looked quickly to the breast of the body seeing the gash of the knife amid other blackened and purple wounds. Other Significant Conditions was footnoted with the number 2 explaining that such condition, or conditions, while contributing to the death, was not related to the disease or condition causing death. Two notes of Vietnamese piasters, also bloody and ragged, were included in the file. A soiled envelope corner poked from the amassed paperwork. Myrtle opened the torn, addressed envelope peeling the contents apart and began to read.

August 17, 1966
Dear Andrea,
I am sorry I haven't written since July. I haven't been convenient to a mail drop of late. Cherokee country Things have been hectic and I'll explain hectic later. Yes. I still carry the crucifix you gave me at aduation. I don't use the chain it came with but it taped in an ammo pouch. I don't wear any ing around my nec is carrying some kind of

token, medal, lucky rabbit's foot. There's a special meaning ere in tough times. One of my buds wears a Sig Heil. You know ow I bounced the ball 3 ti s before shooting freet not 2, not 7, just 3. Same here. I put a lot of emp is on brushing *my teeth these days, no matter the time. In June Graydon got hit in both legs, severed his femoral artery in the right leg. Harper (I've told you about him) worked on him and ran a bottle of albumin. Graydon was gasping and going into shock. I started giving him mouth to mouth. He vomited in my mouth. I couldn't help gagging and crawled away vomit myself. You can guess the rest. It was more the leg wounds. I could taste and smell the LRRP ration he had eaten an hour earlier, or so back on the trail and noticed later a kind of green on his teeth. My thoughts went I don't want die with green scum on my teeth. Crazy, Huh? So, over 3 months the need to have teeth if I should get zapped, brushing, has taken on a different meaning. Now if I brush my teeth I won't die. Cleanest teeth in Vietnam. Vooodoooo. Wooooooo. I hope you aren't disturbed by these confessions. As always, if I can't tell you, who can I tell. Will send* you *the team picture I promised.*

Tell Diana, Chloe, Jurnee and Chris HI and Kisses.

I love you.

F.

She stared at the blotched erasures of the letter and then looked for the first time at the dead soldier's face. It was swollen and pocked. Some mandibular and maxillary bone with teeth were exposed by missing lips. The recesses of the mouth were clotted with blood or other materials. Myrtle looked closely at the gaping smile of teeth and saw a bile-colored vestige. The eyes were open, but a large patch of flesh was torn down from the left temporal area eroding partially over the left eye. The hair from the sidewall gave the upper eyelid the appearance of having an ill-fitted and grotesque toupee and, paired with the pale furrows of exposed skull, the face a frown.

Myrtle sorted *DD Form 894* from a filing of blank forms to provide fingerprint documentation from the corpse in testimony of the dental identification already completed. Without washing her hands, she pulled on a pair of surgical gloves. She then took into her hands the right hand of Sergeant Cooper and began to work at the tightly clenched fingers and thumb attempting to break the rigor of the death-stiffened muscles. She noticed that the thumbnail was fractured to the cuticle and the index finger lacked a fingernail. Two fingers appeared misshapen. The right wrist was abraded and bruised extending about to the elbow.

Myrtle drew a bowl of warm water from a scrubbing tub tap and placing the hand in it, bathed and massaged it, attempting to coax the rigor from it. The hand would not open and further bathing only wrinkled the fingerprints. To get to the ridge detail she would have to cut the hand. Myrtle took a scalpel from a line of scalpels on the presentation table and made a cut at the second joint on the inner side of each of the four fingers. She repeated this between the thumb and index finger. She then pressed the fingers and thumb to the pallet top and pressed the weight of her fist to the back of the hand. This straightened the hand. After drying and inking the fingers she placed *Form* 894 in a spoon cardholder and rolled the encircled form over the cutaneous whorls of Sergeant Cooper's fingers, the motion identical to that of her middle finger in the adjustment of her lipstick.

An Armed Forces DJ announced the AFRVN morning show, Small World, and music by somebody, vocals by Frank Sinatra:

This night could be be - yond for - get - ting
If the two of us were here.

—Good morning, Specialist Jones. Myrtle turned. Captain Neil Runberg, the forensic pathologist, his longer-than-the-Army-liked-it hair in morning disarray, stood eyeing the body of Felix Cooper over her left shoulder. Over six feet tall, slender and with a walk that resembled a slow emu, Runberg didn't have much sympathy with the Army and its regulations.

—Good morning Captain Runberg, Myrtle closed the file and replaced it on a table of equipment trays and surgical instruments.

—He sniffed. You can bathe a decomposing cadaver in good perfume and it still smells like rotting meat on a bed of roses. Ain't helped by two million Vietnamese shitting in the river next door. He stroked at a heavy scar that ran from his left lip to his jaw line, the result of a shaving accident he told Myrtle the first time she inquired.

—I must have acclimated. Have you seen this yet? She picked up the file and offered it to Runberg.

—Yeh, Captain Runberg nodded. Jarvis gave it to me at Property Depot when I came in this morning. Hearing Sinatra on the radio he held his hands up and began singing in an exaggerated baritone:

Full moon and emp - ty arms_____
To - night I'll use the mag - ic moon to wish up - on_____

—You know this tune was lifted from Rachmaninoff's Piano Concerto Number Two? The *meno mosso* passage in the finale. He hummed the same tune that had accompanied the phrase, Full moon and emp - ty arms:

Dah-duh-dah-dah-duh-dah.

—Yeh. A beautiful piece of music, Rachmaninoff's Second. You read the file?

Myrtle nodded.

—This one's really messed up. Makes you wonder what he was up to. There were six of them and six died.

—He was a snake eater. A volunteer for suicide, Runberg said, as he picked up an autoclaved smock.

—Suicide?

—Green Berets. They drop'em in small units deep in enemy territory to collect intelligence and maybe more. When they're detected in the middle of an enemy force of hundreds, even thousands, bad things happen. This soldier, what's left of him, and his buddies are the real idealists in this war. No mission too difficult, no sacrifice too great. You know what I mean?

—Is there something wrong with that? Myrtle asked.

—Apparently. Look what it got him.

—But he died for an honorable cause? Myrtle looked at Runberg for an affirmation. Didn't he?

Runberg turned toward Myrtle with a frown.

—You think they look worse than this for a dishonorable one?

Myrtle shrugged her shoulders and nodded her head indecisively.

—The 17th of August. He wrote that letter Wednesday. This letter.

She picked up again the file jacket and pulled the blotched sheaf written by Cooper from the file.

—Some strange stuff about brushing his teeth. I understand the basketball thing though. Like avoiding a crack in the sidewalk in hopscotch.

—Step on a crack and break your mother's back?

—Yeah. Something like that.

—You were seeking the fortunate event. Calling on the gods.

Myrtle looked at Runberg.

—Two unrelated events occur. You wear a charm or brush your teeth. The grenade going off next to you hits everybody but you. You make connections. The fastening onto the fortunate event associated with the object or behavior is the start of superstition or religion. Where chance and circumstances are not fully controlled by knowledge, man is more likely to resort to magic. There are certain types of occupations involving risk, uncertainty or fear, which are particularly liable to superstition. Soldiers, sailors, athletes, actors, to name a few.

—Brush your teeth and live longer?

—Yes. Wearing protective charms and amulets, performing ritual preparations.

Myrtle frowned.

—How does all that start?

—Someone making meaning out of meaningless coincidence.

A business card fell to the tabletop from the file containing the letter. It was embossed with a skull bearing a Green Beret and a scroll advertising *Murphy's Rules of Combat*.

—Myrtle scanned the contents and said, Listen. She read Murphy's rules of combat:

1. *When in doubt, empty your magazine.*
2. *Never share a foxhole with anyone braver than you are.*
3. *If your attack is going well, it's an ambush.*
4. *If you are forward of your position, the artillery will fall short.*
5. *Incoming fire has the right of way.*
6. *Friendly fire—isn't.*
7. *Radios will fail as soon as you need fire support desperately.*
8. *The only thing more accurate than incoming enemy fire is incoming friendly fire.*
9. *Make it tough for the enemy to get in and you can't get out.*
10. *Professional soldiers are predictable, but the world is full of* amateurs.

—Sounds like someone taking notice of meaningful coincidence, Runberg said. We got our tape recorder?

—Here. She fingered at the voice-activated CIA Continental Uher 4,000L tape recorder and switched it to the foot trundle for start and stop. Are you ready?

—Not yet.

Captain Runberg pulled a green rubber apron from a clotheshorse peg and welding goggles from an adjoining peg.

—Want an apron?

As he said this, he handed one over to Myrtle. He fitted himself pulling the inner tube strap of the goggles behind his head and snapped it several times. He put on a pair of surgical gloves snapping all powdered latex fingers on each hand repeating this exercise with another pair and picked up a scalpel. Myrtle pulled at the fingers of her gloves having donned the green butcher's apron with rubber straps tugging down in the ellipses of her shoulders.

Captain Runberg cleared his throat over the beveled face of the corpse.

—This guy was, what? Twenty years old?

—1946. Yes, twenty. Myrtle answered.

—Uhh. We're a day late.

—A day late?

—The psychologist knows everything and does nothing. The surgeon knows nothing and does everything. The dermatologist knows nothing and does nothing. The pathologist knows everything but is always a day late.

—You don't have a high regard for dermatologists.

—That was a medical school ditty. I don't know why they picked on dermatologists.

—Are you ready? Myrtle looked at her watch.

—What time is it? Runberg asked.

—Saigon Military Standard Time. 0915, Myrtle said.

—Okay. I am identifying the body by the tag tied around the right wrist. The name is Felix Cooper, Sergeant, U.S. Army.

Runberg snipped the tag wire with surgical scissors letting it drop to the floor.

—Date of death, Thursday, August 18, 1966.

He described the superficial appearance of the body naming the various wound types and locations. He probed the torn and drawn flesh pulling down from the orbit arch, the mandible and maxillary exposure and denoted the names of each wound. He reached a finger into the mouth and pulled at its contents removing a shard of black flesh. He handed this to Myrtle and she placed it on the dissection table to the head of the platform.

—Looks like penis. We'll have it analyzed. Make sure. He caught a load of shrapnel in the upper chest and neck from a grenade.

Runberg draped a blue hand towel over the face of Cooper. He described the knife wound in the center of Cooper's chest and the gunshot wound entrance high right of his umbilicus.

—Man, they did him a job.

He looked at the pit of flesh marking the site of the genitalia and noted perfunctorily the excision by blunt instrument of Cooper's penis and testes.

—They must have used his knife to do this surgery.

He reached to the wrists of the body and rubbed his gloved thumbs along the punctured and swollen contours tracing gently the black and blue on Cooper's forearms. Runberg looked at Myrtle.

—Did the records use the word crucifixion?

—I don't think so. Myrtle said

—This guy was crucified you know? Someone went to a lot of trouble to nail him to a mangrove stump. I wonder why?

—And why him and not one of the others, or one of the three Vietnamese? Myrtle asked.

—I don't know about nailing him up but picking him out of the line-up had something to do with natural selection. He was the tallest, blondest.

—The others *were* Vietnamese, weren't they?

—Two Americans. They're in incubation now. The others might have been tribe folk.

Runberg placed a finger on the scabbed chest wound.

—How about that map note piked in his chest?

—We have your x-rays and we think we know the problem. Jesus. Sick. Myrtle said.

—A monstrous sense of humor for a monstrous war, but probably just paybacks. Some American units have special-made card decks containing 52 Aces of Spades with the unit's patch. They impale these cards in the bodies of the dead enemy after battle.

—Why?

—The Ace of Spades has some symbolic meaning for the Vietnamese, or I think it does and it's degrading.

He inserted the point of the scalpel at the head of the left humerus and cut to below the left nipple medially, repeated this from the right shoulder to right nipple then finished the letter

"Y" down the mid-line through the belly button to the empty pubis. He pulled back the skin and muscle tissue exposing the costachondral cartilage on the ribs and removed the chest plate with a small saw taken from the presentation table. Taking up a new scalpel he began to cut connectors from all the organs removing them in a mass from the thyroid down to the urinary bladder and rectum dictating as he went. As he did this Myrtle began scooping the organs from the cavities placing them on the dissecting table. She stopped and shook her head.

—God must be dead, she murmured.

—Dead? Runberg asked. Well, not quite as popular as He once was according to the Beatles.

—I just read that? But John Lennon apologized for saying they were more popular than Jesus.

—I don't know if popular was the right word.

—Didn't stop America from burning their records.

—Yea. Well, it ain't quite as bad as Nietzsche saying God is dead, and now? Myrtle Jones? The edges of Runberg's eyes crinkled behind the welding goggles.

—I didn't mean dead so much as, as, well, I can't see God associated with these things. Not the God I was brought up believing in, Myrtle explained.

—What other God is there? Runberg moved to the dissection table to inspect the organs, which were in the pathway of the projectile that entered Cooper's belly, then he returned to the corpse.

—Cooper was shot from some distance.

He pointed to about five centimeters below the transpyloric plane on Cooper's right side where a coarse wound opening was evident on the abdominal sheath before he pulled it back. He cut quickly through the right lateral border of the rectus sheath on both sides of the wound.

—The projectile lost some speed. See the flattening effect here. It also entered at a trajectory from ten or more degrees below the victim. Runberg was cutting along the wound line on a trail through the fatty deposits of the greater omentum.

—The bullet died here in the right renal cortex severing the right ureter. With a hemostat he pulled a flattened piece of blackened metal from the right kidney.

—That's what took him down. The grenade must have come later. For the others. If they crucified him after this, he wouldn't have felt anything. Where the hell did they find nails in the middle of a swamp?

—Runberg looked up at Myrtle. He stroked at his chin with the back of a gloved hand. Strange you should have said that.

—What?

—That God must be dead.

—What?

—He did die. Two thousand years ago. The servants of some Roman physicians who believed it might have special properties stole the body. Would be interesting to know exactly what they were looking for.

—Oh, bullshit, Neil, Myrtle said.

—No. Some legend that a man named Joseph of Arimethea took the body from the cave. Perhaps they stole it from him. True, or not, I can give you a good estimate of what they would have found.

—What?

—A hemohidrosis on the body. A rare condition caused by extreme stress. Ruptured capillaries. Looked like a ruby flush, the one you see around the neck in spinal meningitis. Remember that Vietnamese baby? The body would have had deep stripe-like lacerations on the back and buttocks with an inferomedial direction to the wounds. From a beating with a short whip with several braided leather thongs of various lengths in which sharp pieces of sheep bone were tied at intervals. Deep contusions where the bones cut into the skin and subcutaneous tissues finally tearing into the skeletal muscles. Fragments of the bone were imbedded in His wounds. An examination of the head revealed lacerations of the face, fracture of the nasal cartilage and back of the head with minute imbedded fragments of the Zizyphus spine.

—Jesus? Where are you getting this from? Myrtle asked conducting fluids to the platform moat.

—From MaMaLuJo, he said. If you've ever read the three or four versions of it, you' have to say that it sounds close, wouldn't you?

—MaMaLuJo! What the hell is that?

—The Bible. Short for Matthew, Mark, Luke and John. Okay, I'm just bullshittin you. Pathologists have been doing guesswork autopsies on Jesus for decades now. I read several of them in medical school, Runberg said, continuing to inspect the corpse.

He did an arc midline incision exposing multiple metallic fragments in the subcutaneous tissue of the chest and in the pectoral muscles. He noted fragments 1 to 3 mm in diameter and that the clavicles were fragmented bilaterally and that the left chest had approximately 200 cc's of blood and the right chest 600 cc's.

—There are fractures of the following ribs; left anterior 3,4,5; right 3rd anteriorly with metallic fragments 2 to 3 mm in diameter. The right transverse process of the 6th, or is it 7th thoracic vertebra, make it 6th, is chipped. Tip of knife lodged in spine, pierced the spinous process and nicked the ventral ramus of the 6th.

Curious about the heart from the state of the cavity he moved to the dissecting table and picked it up. He placed it on a gram scale. The radio announced the time; *10:30 am Saigon Standard Time*; introduction of a vocal by Larindo Almeida.

—Who the hell's that?

—Never heard of him, her, Myrtle answered.

—The heart weighs 250 grams. The knife passage missed the heart entirely. There are two perforations in the left ventricle from metal fragments. They are 1 and 2 mm in diameter on the anterior surface and 2 and 3 mm in diameter posteriorly. Opening the left ventricle demonstrates a traumatic rupture of the papillary muscles. The heart valves are delicate. Look at this. Early atherosclerosis of the anterior descending branch of the left coronary artery. Damn! Wouldn't expect that.

Myrtle began weighing the lungs and liver.

—I wonder if Christ had atherosclerosis of the anterior descending branch of the left coronary artery?

–Yeah? Runberg hesitated. Now that would be interesting. Christ facing a different death, if he hadn't faced Golgotha. I never thought about the gods suffering from disease, or old age.

He was now inspecting the lungs of Cooper.

—The trachea and bronchi are filled with gastric contents and there are small metallic fragments beneath the pleura.

—Wonder what Christ was eating at the last supper? Myrtle asked as she stared at the excised respiratory tree.

—Probably fig cake, gum arabic, a few cc's of wine mixed with myrrh. Given as a mild analgesic before His hands and feet were nailed to the cross. And a big helping of crow.

—Crow?

—For the big mistake. Okay. Skip that one.

—You said hands. Was he nailed through the hands?

—No. A Frenchman named Barbet working with amputated arms demonstrated that the only way the weight of a nailed body could be supported was by nailing it through the wrists. Place called the space of Destot. The nailed hands were impaled at the wrist between carpal bones and radius. The nail transected the median nerve and impaled the flexor longus without breaking the wrist bones. Barbet also discovered that the nail hitting the median nerve caused the thumb to contract into the palm.

—The Vietnamese knew something about Barbet and crucifixion then, Myrtle said touching Cooper's right wrist. They hit Destot's space and the median nerve right on the head.

—Yeah. There were also fractures in two or three fingers on both hands from the smashing effect of an off-mark mallet. The feet were impaled in the second intermetatarsal space with one foot nailed on top of the other. The right foot must have been the top foot because there was chipping of the cuboid and a fracture of the 3rd metatarsal from the force of the mallet.

—Cooper?

—No. Christ.

—God. That's a detail you wouldn't think of. Smashed hands and feet. She pointed at Cooper's hands. He had smash injuries, didn't he?

—Yeah. Whatever they used to hammer the spikes home busted him a couple of times in the hands. Christ had crabbed thumbs. I saw a picture of a shroud, the Shroud of Turin. They say it was the burial cloth that covered Christ. The thumbs were crabbed into the palms. Of course, crucifixion was as common as the cold in Christ's time. It's not like they worked out the kinks on, allegedly, him.

—What explains his legs? Myrtle pointed to the denuded leg bones of Cooper.

—There's a small snapping crab indigenous to the marsh waters of Vietnam called *ca ro*. They've eaten the flesh of the feet and legs. Would have had a hard time nailing his feet under water.

—Jesus, They may as well have.

Runberg touched the adductor magnus, femoral vessels, rectus femoris, vastus medialis as he inspected Cooper's right leg above the knee. He picked up the bladder and turned it over.

—Empty. Self-drained at death.

Blowwwwww, illllllllllll wind, blow away.

Runberg started humming over the strong and pure voice of Ella Fitzgerald.

—DAMN! That lady can sing.

—The Small World host announced: And that was Ella Fitzgerald with the Billy May Orchestra from Ella Fitzgerald Sings the Harold Arlen Song Book. The time is 11:15 am Saigon Standard.

The wound to Cooper's groin had shaved the genitalia flat with the adductor longus to the raphe. Runberg noted the exposure of the posterior scrotal vessels and nerves as well as the bulbospongiosus overlying the bulb of the penis and remarked that the anus was intact. A flower of cotton batting protruded from it as well as from the rectum on the now visible, excised, inner wall. He gave a low whistle.

—He could have died for a lot of different reasons, Myrtle said.

She began to replace the cut and inspected viscera back into the body cavities.

—Cooper? Runberg asked.

—No, Christ.

—Huh-uh. Two ways. Suffocation and a spear wound to the heart. When they crucify you, you can't breathe. The weight of the body hanging from the cross hinders passive exhalation. To blow out you have to lift your body by pushing up on the feet and by flexing the elbows and adducting the shoulders.

Myrtle raised her arms and bounced up and down on her toes practicing the movement.

—We don't usually have to think about breathing but hanging fixes the intercostal muscles in an inhalation state and that interferes with passive exhalation. Having to physically assist breathing on a cross causes extreme pain in the feet and the damaged median nerves in the wrists. Every respiration requires flexing and adducting which soon leads to fatigue. When you can't lift up any longer you can't exhale. And then. Suffocation.

—Do you think Cooper was alive when they nailed him to the tree? Myrtle asked.

—No. The North Vietnamese, or whoever, reversed the Passion Play. Killed him then crucified him.

—The knife wound to his chest alone could have killed him?

—True, but that was an afterthought.

—What about the spear to Christ's side?

—That finished the job. An eyewitness said there was a spurt of blood and water from the wound. The blood would have been from the blood distended, thin-walled right ventricle when the spear entered the thorax piercing the right lung and pericardium. The water was from pleural and pericardial effusions. Just on that testimony alone I can tell you that Christ was in hypovolemia and acute heart failure.

Runberg placed the heart back into the body of Cooper and pulling the goggles from his face and head removed his gloves and lab clothing finishing the nearly two hours of autopsy.

—Who's the civilian embalmer on duty?

—Mr. Arnold, Myrtle said. She threw her butcher's apron and smock to the floor.

—He can repair this damage. Runberg placed his apron and goggles on the specimen table. I'm getting hungry. I didn't eat breakfast. You?

—Just coffee.

Myrtle and Runberg walked one after the other to the embalming atrium and entered the refrigeration unit threading through other members of the mortuary company who had filtered in after their arrival.

—How about that Buddhist restaurant on Hung Vuong Street? Get some of that vegetarian pho.

—Vietnamese soup. I don't think so.

—They make American too.

—You know Neil. I can't help thinking that Cooper's death was more terrible than Christ's.

—The manner of death? Yeah. Definitely would have been some concerted pain there. Christ took a beating but went a little quicker.

—I'm suddenly feeling like I'm missing something here. Two thousand years of my religion depends on the death of Christ on a cross, the greatest sacrifice of all. But seeing and hearing what I did today makes that sacrifice seem such a pointless thing.

—Or a symbolic thing. But there was one big difference, said Neil.

He pulled on his baseball cap with two silver bars before stepping from the darkened mortuary into the tropical sun.

—And what would that be? Myrtle said, reaching her right forearm to her eyes to shield them from brightness of the light.

—Captain Runberg said, with a laugh. Christ was resurrected.

IMMORTALITY

"My Name is Ozymandias, king of kings,
Look on my works, ye Mighty and despair!"
Nothing besides remains. Round the decay
Of that colossal wreck, boundless and bare
The lonely and level sands stretch far away.

—Percy B. Shelly, *Ozymandias*

I.

Professor Derek Friday and his wife, Alice Friday, sat in the early hours of Saturday morning watching television between dozes in the waiting room of the intensive care unit of Ithaca Memorial Hospital. Their ten-year old son, Bobby, was battling complications of infantile liver disease.

Something in the late, late movie caught Mrs. Friday's attention. *The Deadly Mantis* starred Craig Stevens, Alix Talton, William Hopper and a prehistoric praying mantis bigger than a B-52 frozen in an Arctic iceberg.

Dr. Jackson: *All right, Professor, you know as well as I do that if a living organism is frozen quickly enough, it is theoretically possible to stop the living protoplasm from changing their geometrical patterns which always happens when death occurs.*

Professor: *Theoretically? Yes.*

Dr. Jackson: *Is it unreasonable, then, to ask yourself whether the mammoth mightn't have remained alive all those years and it was the Siberians who killed them before they had a chance to thaw out and breathe again?*

Professor: *Cute. You believe this?*

Dr. Jackson: *Well. I don't disbelieve it and I'll go along with it until someone comes up with a better theory. Look, five men have vanished. To die is one thing. To disappear without a trace suggests complete destruction.*

The giant mantis was thawed and winging its way to America to fill an empty belly. But *The Deadly Mantis* was only an omen. It was the even later talk show that delivered the coincidental and almighty revelation. It featured a Dr. Robert Honeyweather. The show's host, Jack Smiley, was questioning Dr. Honeyweather for a full understanding of cryogenics, the new science of freezing. Dr. Honeyweather explained nitrogen freezing, asanguineous total-body perfusion, cryo-capsules, maintenance insurance, and immortality.

Dr. Honeyweather: *The point here is to deliver the patient, the dead, to a more advanced medical science. Since we can't bring this science to the patient, we have to bring the patient to the future. Storage in liquid nitrogen will keep him essentially unchanged for an indefinite period of time, except for some freezing damage. If our optimism proves warranted and medical science has learned how to cure or repair all damage—including the effects of old age—then those who die now will have indefinitely extended life in the future.*

Jack Smiley: *By the way, just how cold is liquid nitrogen?*

Dr. Honeyweather: *320 to 380 degrees below zero Fahrenheit.*

Jack Smiley: *What do you say to those people who say, Rubbish. You're taking advantage of grieving, or hopelessly optimistic families who are willing to pay what is probably an exorbitant price for this service? Or the scientists who say that cryonic suspension preserves meat not cells?*

Dr. Honeyweather: *Yes, those are good points. There may be failure, but the freezer is more attractive than the grave, even if one has doubts about the future capabilities of science. With bad luck, people who have elected cryonic preservation will simply remain dead, as they would have in the grave.*

Jack Smiley: *Yeh. Like an undertaker I know always says. I haven't had a funeral yet that failed. (Ha, Ha, Hah!)*

Amazed, Alice Friday looked at her husband. "Did you follow all of that?"

He turned to her, raising his chin from his cupped hand. "Yes. Poor grieving families. We don't fit the profile, yet."

"I'm serious Derek," Alice said. "I'm serious."

She looked at this rough-hewn man, who combined powerful intellect with great physical strength, and knew he would laugh at this idea even if it had already registered with him, and it probably had. The long trail that brought him to Cornell University where he now lectured in Southeast Asia Studies led from a farm in some snow-covered corner of Montana to the jungles of South Vietnam then through the ivy halls of Columbia University. He served in U.S. Army

Special Forces as a young officer with a secret mission force, MACV-Studies and Observation Group, a unit during the Vietnam War conducting illegal cross-border reconnaissance, prisoner-snatch operations, electronic monitoring and chaos. He had led a recon team, in violation of the provisions of the *1954 Geneva Accord*, to invade by stealth the allegedly neutral dominions of Cambodia and Laos.

He had entered these countries, swollen with the staging armies of North Vietnam, by way of night parachute jumps and heliborne insertions. Those forays exposed him to the very worst in Vietnam combat, but because these operations were conducted under the umbrella of the Central Intelligence Agency with layers of unit masquerade set up for deniability, former operators were sworn into eternal pacts of secrecy. The professor sneered at those proscriptions and described for Alice the true scope of the moral engagement of American Forces in Southeast Asia, with the *caveat*, "Don't tell Huntley and Brinkley."

And now he was at Cornell, far above Cayuga Lake, ambling between the lecture hall and the library. Cornell—overlooking the blue-green waters of the winding lake with green and brown checkerboard fields rising up the slope of West Hill.

"I am going to have Bobby cryogenically frozen. If there is any possibility, he can experience a full life without pain and disease, even in a remote future, I will do this." She relayed this with an urgency and matter-of-factness that startled the professor.

He was slow to answer, staring hard at this woman he married while still a teen-ager; the only woman he'd ever had eyes for from the moment he saw her hugging books to her chest in his fifth-grade class. This was the woman who'd accompanied him through thick and thin since, and the one who'd absorbed most deeply the pain and the anger over Bobby's illness. For even at ten years of age, Bobby had begun to exhibit the same traits of talent, strength and independence his father had and so much hope was place on his little shoulders. Now, there had been convincing signs tonight; the ice-frozen mantis, the evangelical Dr. Honeyweather, and a woman holding out hope against hope for their dying son.

He knew what she intended and offered a weak protest, "Cicero said that nothing that has an end is long."

"I don't give a rat's ass what Cicero said," Alice blurted, angered, then seeing Derek's startled gaze, said, "You know what I mean."

"I was fighting that one last doubt." The professor said. Life had always been just another roll of the dice for him. "You tell me what we are going to do and we'll do it."

Alice looked at Derek as she blinked back tears and whispered, "I love you."

II.

Alice spent long hours in the following week at Cornell's Olin Library developing a list of contacts for Bobby's cryogenic preservation, and eventually, her own and the Professor's. She joined the New York Cryonics Society, purchased a family cryogenic maintenance insurance policy, and consorted with the Immortality Research and Compilation Association. But most important, she set out to gain the assistance of the physician who was overseeing Bobby's care at Ithaca Memorial. The Immortality Research Association made clear how important good medical assistance was—within minutes, or seconds of death—as soon as possible, to complete the perfusion, cooling and freezing of the patient.

As Bobby's health declined, Alice presented her plan, and a learned treatise (*Asanguineous Total-Body Perfusion*) she had found in the *Journal of American Medical Association,* to Bobby's physician, Dr. Healy. She obtained his agreement, with a little resistance, to follow the guidelines for cryonic interment of her son after his death.

Within forty-eight hours of the culmination of Alice's logistical assault Bobby gave up his struggle. Within a minute of Bobby's death Dr. Healy started cardiopulmonary resuscitation and put him on a heart-lung machine. Cut-downs were done on both femoral arteries and veins. The left femoral artery was connected to a pressure recorder. Both femoral arteries were cannulated and the right femoral artery cannula was connected to a pressure transducer. After he had opened the chest, Dr. Healy cannulated the right atrium and heparin was administered intravenously.

Using a tubing pump, Dr. Healy began forcing a buffered glucose-dextran solution through a blood exchanger into the left femoral artery. Arterial profusion was begun and the atrial cannula was opened and the entire venous return was allowed to drain into a siliconized receptacle. The body rapidly cooled to 59 degrees Fahrenheit in about 30 minutes.

Dr. Healy finally drilled a pinhole in Bobby's skull above his left ear to insert a temperature probe to monitor the descent of temperature. At one hour, Bobby was removed from the heart-lung bypass and submerged in a bath of silicone oil where he remained for a day and a-half. This cooled his body temperature to approximately that of dry ice, or about minus 108 degrees.

Dr. Healy and two assistants removed Bobby on the second day, wrapped him in two pre-cooled sleeping bags and placed him inside a protective duraluminum pod. They then lowered him into a unit filled with liquid nitrogen. Bobby gradually cooled over the next 24 hours to a negative 321 degrees.

On the third day, at this stabilized temperature, Bobby was transferred to a storage container called a Dewar. The professor obtained the Dewar, like all other specialty materials needed. Bobby was sealed in the Dewar capsule and prepared for shipping to a cryo-preservation mausoleum recently opened in the Washington Memorial Cemetery in Russia, New York. The storage mausoleum already held more than a hundred cryonic adventurers upon a wooded hillside a couple of hundred miles northeast of Ithaca and was expected to house thousands more. Alice and Professor Friday accompanied their son for interment in the mausoleum, said their good-byes, and returned to Ithaca.

Within two years of Bobby's death, Alice Friday succumbed to a heart attack. Professor Friday, keeping word and faith with her plan, coordinated her full body perfusion and cryogenic encapsulation with Dr. Healy. He transported her to the mausoleum at Russia to rest in waiting with Bobby. Professor Friday made his way back to Ithaca alone.

III.

In 1908, an asteroid about 60 meters across entered the earth's atmosphere and burst apart over the Tunguska Valley in Siberia, Russia. The explosion was reputed to have been heard as far away as London. The area below the explosion is still marked by burnt trees sprawled in a region over 50 miles across. Circumstantial evidence suggests that fires were ignited up to 40 miles from the endpoint by the intense burst of radiant energy. The devastation was enormous.

Two years after the death of Alice Friday, an asteroid two kilometers across plummeted into the earth's atmosphere over Bhopal, India at more than 20 miles per second. The equation for calculating the kinetic energy liberated by such an impact is ½ *mv squared*, where *m* is the mass of the object and *v* is the incoming velocity. Assuming a density of three grams per cubic centimeter, as known from meteorites, and the velocity of 20 miles per second (72,000 mile per hour), a two-kilometer-wide object would strike earth with a shock equivalent to a billion times the energy released in the 1945 Hiroshima bomb-blast.

Such was the case at Bhopal, which hides almost in the center of India. The impact crater, which absorbed Bhopal, measured more than 65 miles in diameter. Kanpur and Lucknow almost 200 miles to the north were utterly destroyed and the same for Hyderabad to the south, and Ahmedabad to the west. Titanic tidal floods reaching heights greater than 500 feet overcame Calcutta and all coastal cities from the Burmese peninsula to Mozambique. Every city and town within a 400-mile radius was inundated by the shockwave, wind and fire blown out from the center.

An enormous fireball ejected rocks and steam into the atmosphere and jarred the earth's crust so savagely that it triggered earthquakes and tsunamis round the world. Vast clouds of dust erupted into the stratosphere and beyond. There slowly formed a total daytime darkness over the earth. Temperatures began to drop worldwide. Nitric acid produced from the burning of atmospheric nitrogen in the impact fireball began to rain back to earth acidifying lakes, streams and the surface layer of the oceans. Darkness hung over the globe for more than a year and a terrible winter settled over all the lands of planet earth.

IV.

The grain fields of the world produced nothing for more than two years. Finally, the long darkness of the days began to lift and sunlight filtered through giving surface dwellers a carp's-eye view of the sky. Snow had been general in New York State since the cataclysm. It was estimated, last heard over a still transmitting radio station, that more than three-quarters of the world's population was lost. Billions were dead.

The blast and the terrible violence of the collision was not so much the culprit as starvation and the hardships of the eternal winter. The small clumps of surviving population were autonomous centers now, small feudalisms spread out as last outposts of civilization. All governments had collapsed, and all transportation systems, all manufacturing abandoned. The world financial markets were destroyed and monetary trade ceased. If there existed a world market, it was one of relics. The only important marker of trade in this age was the goods, and guns. If you did not have the goods, you could not buy them, but with a gun you could take them.

From above, Ithaca appeared to be a city buried beneath snow. The tarmac of a few roads could be seen where men had worn them down for walkways, or the peeking sun had begun to thaw them through to the blacktop. Where once, along West Hill, the headlights of moving automobiles glittered through the trees, darkness; no trains entering on Aurora Street, or Dryden Road; no aircraft in landing patterns over Taughannock Boulevard.

Movement in the leafless elms just southwest of Ithaca revealed men and women, on what had once been Elmira Road, entering and leaving from under the exposed roof of a giant, log lodge with a remnant neon sign astride a rear chimney.

A group of twenty or more people camouflaged by white clothing trudged northward up Route 13 toward Cortland. Many of those leaving the lodge were struggling to catch up with this group.

In the lead was a large man distinguished from the group by a slate-gray Parka with a fabric crusader mask. Perched under his left arm was an AK-47 and strapped to his back, a camouflaged, mounted crewman bag. Three other members of the group carried weapons.

The patrol passed two nights in this trek to the north. On the third day in late afternoon under a sky that had loosened even more sunlight through the ever-present haze, they came into land that swelled in snow covered fields and pastures edged by small stands of pine and fir. The leader walked with assured and quicker step toward one of the stands of firs. At the breech of the woods an opening allowed a glimpse of a wrought-iron fence and a gate capped with iron molded letters announcing,

WASHINGTON
MEMORIAL
CEMETERY

The leader walked through the gate and moved between monuments and raised spires peeking through piled snow banks uphill toward a large mausoleum. It was abutted by a new addition finished in block and steel. As he reached this structure, he turned to his followers and waved them forward. He pulled the crusader mask from his face to address the gathering.

Professor Friday said only a few words and moved into the building through an undoored aisle between Doric columns. The three gun-carrying adjutants followed him. Minutes passed before the four reemerged pulling a sleek metallic pod. The crowd watched silently. Professor Friday stood at one end of the capsule and lifting his AK-47, butt first, smashed at the tip. A faint popping, like the cork from a champagne bottle, echoed against snow-drifted tombstones. He pulled from a scabbard beneath his parka a long knife and inserted it in a hidden seam on the pod. He pried and with both hands forced the capsule open. He jumped back from an erupting cloud of mist and liquid. He spoke to the crowd again and they, removing knives and small axes, began to disperse into the treeline surrounding the cemetery to gather firewood.

In the pitch-blackness of night over Russia, light flared against the surrounding firs of the cemetery.

Dancing celebrants cast cavorting silhouettes on the snow and peaking monuments. A huge bonfire raged below the mausoleum and amidst the spikes and spires of memorial stones and tombs now uncovered by the heat. The grounds were scattered with the discarded shells of Dewar containers. Barbecue drums improvised from the metal of the Dewars were full to the overflowing with hissing and spitting meats. Professor Friday stood at the top-most step of the mausoleum and watched the feasting mob below.

THE KING TEACHES HIS EDUCATED SON A LESSON

In spite of his father's wish that his education be entirely religious and pragmatic, the young Frederick, with the help of his tutor Jacques Duhan, procured for himself a three thousand volume secret library of poetry, Greek and Roman classics, and French philosophy to supplement his official lessons.

—MacDonogh, Giles, *Frederick the Great: A Life in Deed and Letters*

(Berlin) —One of the figures in the strange case of Frederick the Second, heir-apparent to the Prussian throne, was executed on the 6th day of this month. Lieutenant Hans Hermann von Katte was found guilty as an accomplice to the Crown Prince's ill-fated flight from Prussia. A Court-martial board, installed at Copenick, returned this verdict on von Katte: "That he did plot and colleague with foreign Courts in aid of said Prince

> and of an intended high crime against the Prussian Majesty itself on the Prince's part; that von Katte's crime amounts to high treason (crimen lease majestatis), that the rule is Fiat justitia et pereat mundus—and that, in brief, von Katte's sentence is here-by declared to be death by the sword and headsman."
>
> —*The Daily Courant,* London, 13 November, 1730

TOUT EST DECOUVERT

A black cupola tipped by a crooked cross—the work of a mad momicks—swayed dizzily from the pentagonal prison walls. Berlin's November air hung turgidly round *Custrin* castle. The five white, window-specked walls peaked through the battered arms of dormant autumn elms. The tangled branches mirrored in the fortress moat cast gnarled reflections on a sentinel lake. Cold water eyed the castle with a hardening glance.

What The Blackbird Saw

Moving aloft from a weathered elm:

The grey, cold air sat heavily on black ringed shale. A lacuna peaked up from guarding walls, the brown belly of the five-sparred gaol. The prison, ringed by barred windows and heavy oak doors, hulked in frozen silence. Beneath the wounded cupola, at the castle's base, hands peered through a grated window.

Winged:

In arching turn past Stygian moat, cross sandbagged marsh, westward by Mother Oder curled *Spree Flus* to the gates of Brandenburg, *Schloss Monjibou* and the tethered city of Berlin.

Smoke plumed Berlin:

Stately towered churches, mud-quayed river vessels, *Leipziger Strasse* in brown rut. Royal Square in busy disarray was flanked on all sides by *fortuna primigenia.* Roman greaves. From Hospital-Market Square, Hackes Market, Kolinish Fish Market and busy cafes leaked fumes of Berlin's suppers. Roasted poultry, braised pork leg folded with gusts of spiced dumplings, eel soup and lean, sizzling bacon. Livers, kidneys, fenneled sausage fried to a succulent turn gathered with scented lentils, buttered mushrooms, leeks and turkish beans in an ossuary high over Berlin.

Below:

The rolling, hillock wood, ungroomed, ran eastward from *Leipziger* wall to *Custrin* on molting limbs, winter nipping at its heels.

The Cymotrichous Heir

Prince Frederick William, *Hohenzollern*, grasped the gunmetal grey bars of his cell window. He peered into the brown bowels of the prison court.

The King's dungeon. My papa. My flesh and blood. He plans to play Salome. Old hoary Phillip. Why they brought me down from the warm upstairs. No meal today. Starve me dead? No. My own father. I pray to thee Father. Coffee. A cup, and. And. Cold eel pie with fish stuffing. The stuffing: bowl of pike, boned, skinned and passed through a fine sieve. And brandy. And bacon, and Frau Racoulle's pie crust with which ....

Raising unfocused eyes, the prince flinched his gaze to a darting shadow.

Blackbird. Away. Eagle me to England o'er Oder, the gates of to chalk white cliffs. Snow soon. Color of the air. The smell of it. The top decorated with pastry and two holes so the steam can escape. Chalk cliffs or Paris. Sign myself Frederic le Philosophe. Voltaire. Katte? Dare not speak the name. He fly too? Quidnunc in the Court of mon oncle.

Brown ground, brown bush, brown scaffold in the brown courtyard. A cutting block rested on the scaffold.

See no hanging arm. Chopping block. Chop. Sever this cord for living. Final cut. Once from my Mother. Once from him. Sever me from myself, the intellect from the extended. Descartes. If a thing thinks then it is. If dead? Ask Aeacus. Why we need the Gods. Volatire. Si Dieu n'existait pas, il faudrait l'inventer. But sweet sausages a moment; onions, buttered bread. Pea soup with bacon. With a pig's ear. The legend. What makes a great pea soup? A spoon will stand up in it. Please.

Frederick turned back to the bare-walled cell. A bent stub of wax jutted from the rough top of a small table in the corner.

His wax. Remains the same. Melt it. Smell it. Tap it. Wax will lead me to myself. Ego sum. Ego existo. I think of sausage therefore I am? Easy to say for a well-fed philosopher. Eggs, boiled, poached. Buttered bread. O. Please. And coffee. I smell now.

Frederick fingered the rippled remains of yellow, candle tallow on the rough-shorn table.

I don't know what it is, but I can see it. I know what sausages are. Death will change me? Same substance, new form—my entelechy. Will Katte? No. He did nothing. My Father's kingdom. Rule it by the rule. Fiat justitia, et pereat mundus. Hang me, slice me, but do not kill me, beg I plead of you. King's son. Ask Joab. He would know. He offered ten but the man said Though he receive a thousand shekels of silver in his hand he would not put forth it against the King's son. Heed him father. Useless. My kingdom for a horse. Fast one make it.

Bare, grey walls, wooden bed with an unstuffed mattress marked the empty room.

No room for laughter gay here. Optimo. Whatever is, is right. Gottfried Wilhelm, affirm me

O grand sensorium. Whatever is, will hurt. Second best of all possible worlds. A horse, a horse.

With quivering thoughts, Frederick's stomach quivered. Hunger—a knotted nothingness conjured up somethingness. Cakes, a grouse in aspic, SAUSAGE, flooded the young heir's senses.

Kartoffelpfannkuchen mit zweiben. Brown crust, fine flake, soft scented. Onion. Eisbein. Fat pig's leg. Smell now. With? With thick-blooded gravy and hunked fresh bread. Large curds of butter, pungent-yellow. Buttered entree. Oysters. Once. The sea coast. O oysters.

Aromas of thought wafted from the dreary cell room into the meal brown court. Some unsniffed coffee dissipated into the darkening sky.

CORYBANTIASM

Recumbent, repentant, submissive, amending. The prince turned to his side curling his legs to his chest under a tattered fragment of cloth. Fresh leather soles peeped from the ragged lump.

All fathers forsaking all sons. The All-Father forsaking the All-Son. Filius Dei unigeniti. On the cross. Spearstruck messenger on a pole. O my Father, why hast thou forsaken me? But he? Miracles. I need one now. Make the dead walk, wine, bread and fish for? How many? Damascus trout, Nineveh perch. I wonder. Forellen Blau. White-fleshed, soft-fleshed. Or like that meunière from Swabia. Lake Constance. Fried in butter. The English have 42 religions and only two sauces. Voltaire said that. How I admire. Did the Jesus Christ walk on waves to fetch the throngs their meal? Pater Ominipotens saved him from Neptune's prongs. Saved him for the cross, land-lubber's spear. Or maybe returned as a mercenary from our dark land in the forces of Tiberius Claudius Nero Caesar, conqueror of Elbe and the Rhine. He lost his legs in Teutoburg Forest when Varus was destroyed by Cherusci but with the aid of certain prosthetics like soldiers I have seen carved with loving hand by the Gadaran cross maker Didymus, or some such, from soft decapolitan pines or some such, did usher in the hydropatetic school of ministry with floating legs? Judas in the cool of a summer morn worked steadily with his Jesus piling green stained stones at the lake's edge in strategic submarine piles from the weathered quay toward the northward swell of Galilee. No matter. Wine from water. Wonder was it white, or red? Fish from? Sleight of hand? Chef. Maitre de maitre-autel. Cunctipotent epicure. I so cold and hungry am.

Breathing fogged breaths, Frederick dozed.

Ghoul's eyes. A starched and wrinkled mouth in a mummy's head. Chinoise? Wu. Murdering dowager. Killed all her sons. Beautiful prose will save me. All-serenest and All-graciousest Father. Forgive me for I have sinned and come short of the glory of reign. My sin. My sin. My most grievous sin. Say it pacific-like. Submissive. On my belly to protect the entrails. Do not cut this navel. This neck. Signed. I sign.

Frederick searched the grey-cold mists of his fitful sleep. He saw his father entreating a row of soldiers tabled in courtly tribunal. Then, where the tribunal had been seated suddenly, sea dripping wet, trident armed, hulked the Sea God.

Poseidon. My Father. Poseidon he implores. I Hippolytus. But for all the wrong reasons. Should I watch the sea? My death from the sea?

From the rough waters lapping at Frederick's cell wall plunged an ember-eyed bull, sea tendrils clinging to its frothy flanks. Frederick jerked. Sleep broken. The watery edges of the room faded, fish-silvery phantoms. A red haze curtained the walls.

A red haze when I awaken. Hellfires burning out there? Old man with a white bush of hair. Woe to you depraved souls. Is Acheron that red river. Red is blood. Mine. The evening smoke is lifting. Tomorrow? Will the crimson band be poured over my eyes? Who is the axeman? Some Russian. A large syphilitic Grozny? Like the roaring lunatic from the Muscovy fringe anointing young Ivan. Call a priest, an inquisitor. Soften me up for the kill. Full of the milk of human kindness then smiles, crossing himself while my head falls. The King, my father, beckoning those cloaked smilers, like Salome. Bring me the head of Katte. No. Bring me the head of my son. Will convert now to that Eastern thought, that Eastern path. If only I could fly.

Like the blackbird. Leave this land of angry men. Smiling angry kings. Go with Katte. Next to Buddha for the night. Fat Oriental omnipotence. Sleep beneath a wide expanse of roof with decorated beams, barbel-mouthed snakes with bright tongues twined about the doorway pillars. In the green night of lotus land, a soft sun, ever sinking red on the forest back. A land of dusk of sleep, of rest. Arena of the forest hart and white-palmed sloat. The evening smoke descends. Small feet patter. The red veil hangs o'er a land of dusk, of rest, of sleep—of sleep.

THE DIREMPTION

Morning light stabbed through Frederick's lone cell window. November's cold, moist fingers kneaded his slumbering form. He muttered in his wakening and heaved, suddenly, upright. Knocking and banging coming from the courtyard opened his eyes and cracked the crust of sleep from their impeded view. Uniformed men of the King's Guard bent, tinkering at the brown-plank scaffold. He turned furtively to face his tormenters.

Knock. Knock. They come. Listen. Quiet. They come. I will go quietly. No Fight. Rant. Go quiet. Dignified. A death fit for the King's son. For a King. Vere dignum et justum est.

The prince could hear the courtyard workers. His breath came in short, thin rasps. Voices seeped from the north entrance to the courtyard. Frederick moved quickly to the barred window of his room. He gripped the fishgrey metal forcing his face against the frosted iron. The gate yard doors to the castle swung open. A small band of King's men led a drab-cloaked figure into the brown courtyard. Frederick strained through the grillwork. The view shook him, shook the bars. He yelled out.

"Katte. Katte. In the name of God, I ask you, stop the execution till I write the King."

Katte. Not me. No. My father knows the truth. Katte. I am the cause of your death? I am. Too late. The King in Berlin has played a monstrous game. As easily stop the sun from rising. O. Poor Katte. Mon cher Katte. Letter useless. All-serenest and . . . . STOP.

Katte's death processional turned toward the prince's window but proceeded slowly to the block. Katte, who had been gazing skyward, now stared long in the direction of the prince's voice.

Frederick cried out. *"Pardonnez-moi, mon cher Kattte.* Oh, that this should be what I have done to you."

Von Katte answered the cell window. "Death is sweet for a prince I love. If I had a thousand lives, how gladly would I lay them down for you." The company of soldiers with Katte in tow continued to the scaffold. Frederick moved at his caging window trying to shake the bars loose.

Soon. Now. It will be done. The murder of an innocent. I will avenge this murder. I will avenge. Dead father. Dead soldiers. Dead priests. Flay them all. Puziel, Guziel, Pdiel, Prziel. I call thee and those six knots, go quickly to that King and put poison in his belly. I wish it. Amen. Selah.

His entreaty to fallen angels departed the universe as von Katte bent over the scaffold block. Raising his eyes to heaven, Katte whispered, "Into thy hands, O my God, I commend my spirit." His head was severed in a single cut. Blood pulsed from his still moving form. A priest, hidden in soldier company, turned his head, a handkerchief held to his flushed face. Frederick knelt, swaying, on his rude, clay floor.

Listen O blood, instead of flowing. Instead of pouring forth. Stop blood. Like a wall. Stop like a hedge. Stop like a reef in the sea. Like stiff sedge in the moss. Like a boulder in the field. Like the pine in the wood. Useless. His head. He is my Baptist. Raise him from the dead? Jesus? The trout man of Galilee. Bloodless. Soft. White. Katte. Soft and white. He said if I had a thousand lives, a thousand shekels. Katte! Where are you? Where will you be hereafter? Too late. Let dead men rest. Do now what the believers do. Criss-cross. Lord have mercy. Christ have mercy. Lord have mercy.

At The Ossuary

The grey-cold air was filled with thick flakes, silvery phantoms falling lightly on the black-ringed shale of the castle. The brown belly of Custrin rested, the tired leopard, while soft whiteness cleansed its bloodied hide. The prison court, ringed by barred windows and heavy oaken doors, hulked in frozen silence. Soft, falling flakes sank by a grated window. White-knuckled hands gripped at the frozen bars.

Snow fell heavily on Custrin and on the lethean marshes guarding the great Oder river and on the forested hills rolling softly to Berlin and on the molded struts of Brandenburg. It soon would cover the brown rut of Leipziger Strasse and the marbled roofs of Royal Square and the tree-lined road from Copenick. It began to rest heavy on the rusty wall of the small churchyard where Hans von Katte made his way in a burlap covered wagon pulled by snow-covered dray horses. There already awaited posing warriors on a crusted monument with stone-carved hair matting with the white of the falling blanket. It drifted to all the stone-banked sepulchers of the dead. It fell slowly, whitely from a bank of blackness overhead to blanket the blackness of the earth.

THE KING TEACHES HIS EDUCATED SON...

AUDIE MURPHY IN SAIGON

War is a racket maintained by those who profit from it.

—Major General Smedley Butler, USMC, (Awarded the Medal of Honor twice)

At the end of the fight is a tombstone white with the name of the late deceased, And the epitaph drear: "A Fool lies here who tried to hustle the East."

—Rudyard Kipling *Naulakha*

SAIGON, Friday, November 1, 1963—Inside his suitcase Lucien Conein had packed hand grenades, a pistol, a special CIA radio and 3,000,000 Vietnamese piasters—roughly $42,000—in escape money for the generals. Moments earlier he had received the two-hour notice and flashed the go code to the tight group with a need to know (no American military men included). When Perry [Mert Perry of Time magazine] drove up, Conein had been arranging for the dispatch of a twelve-man U.S. Special Forces A Team to protect his family if the coup d'tat failed. Then he high-tailed it to the JGS headquarters near Tan Son Nhut airport.

—William Prochnau, *Once Upon a Distant War*

I.

Brewery workers at the Distilleries de l'Indochine hurried to drag ash tarpaulin over palleted bottles stacked about walled yards. One of the members of the last supper, Andrew, or Judas, approached from the office housing Brasseries et Glacieres de l'Indochine waving his opened hand at workers shaking in the wet, cold air.

—Don't cover the bottles. Leave them in the air.

This weather won't last and the beer'll be cold for a day or two. Did the Vietnamese like his beer served cold? Would the bottles explode with expanded liquid in the frozen morning hours? Unusual weather for Vietnam, huh? In the paddy land of Binh Tuy and Tay Ninh, snow-covered the planted hectares of rice, piling higher on ice-

crusted, paddy water. Thin, shivering, green shoots peaked above the blanketing snow. In Bien Hoa and Thu Duc marketplaces, vendors and buyers snapped up available cloth and binding goods. Sandals were snow-proofed with the bindings. Hastily erected tents and verandah pole-frames of the marketplace were collapsing beneath the weight of accumulated snows and bon fires began dotting the town and city streets as populations massed about the roaring flames to warm themselves. The Lao Tam dam was freezing over and the tributaries of the great snow-strewn Mekong showed only glimpses of green and grey waters; Nui Ba-den, rising out of a shallow snow cloud stood like a solitary Alp toward Dau Tieng. The cavern doors to the Holy Temple were lost in the thundering white drifts tumbling through the mountain to the forest floor. Billy Harper rested in one of these vaults, wrapped in white linens waiting on his resurrection, a stone rolled before the mouth. From a mountain vault a single flute sang out over an immense field of whiteness.

A siren blaring from somewhere on the Saigon River awakened a dozing Sergeant First Class Jude Sands from his snowy dream. A lumpy bag of ice, now cold water, had fallen from his face, where he had placed it in the night, to lodge between his neck and the cot he was using in the U.S. Embassy Annex. Shivering and licking the acid-sweet remains of something he had eaten last night, he rose fully dressed and put together his pack and equipment.

He was one of a team of Special Forces soldiers ordered yesterday to the Embassy; brought in for a briefing on security for the real estate of American government "officials" and their families in the greater area of Saigon. Why? Because there was plotting and "coup shit" going on in the air in November 1963.

The briefer at the Annex told Sergeant Sands that his assignment and point of rendezvous was the villa and wife of one of these "officials" on Le Qui Don Street. Mrs. Smith was in her forties, she belonged to a church group called the Assembly of God, and her time was taken up with charitable and religious projects. There were no children, no other family, and he was not the first bodyguard sent to Mrs. Smith in this bloody season of 1963. Since several Buddhist martyrdoms by fire, mob rule had taken Saigon's streets. In the local population, prophecies of doom had spread but no tales of miracles. Burned Buddhists did not rise from the ashes like the Phoenix but were swept into dustpans. He went to the closest bar on Tu Do Street the first night and got drunk then returned to the Annex at a late hour.

II.

He left the Annex on Ham Nghi street early to encounter a beating sun. He entered the thoroughfare of Tu Do Street which ran from the esplanade on the Saigon River through the bar district then past the cathedral of Our Lady of Saigon, the Gia Long Palace, and northwest to a villa on Le Qui Don Street, his point of rendezvous.

He was dressed in *Beo-Gâ'm* dapple, camouflage, jungle fatigues and wore the felt, green beret of U.S. Army Special Forces adorned with a shield of orange, black and white with a metal crest of arrows crossed upon a sword surrounded by a scroll inscribed in Latin, *De Oppresso Liber*. The metal crest indicated he was an enlisted man. Rank chevrons were absent from his tunic. As he walked, he removed his beret, detached the metal crest, and placed it in a pocket. Reaching into a side pocket of his ruck, he removed a set of Captain bars. He attached the rank insignia to the flash on his beret and placed it back on his head, aligning the shield above his left eye.

He carried with him a Swedish Model 45-9mm submachine gun, a bulging ranger ruck-pack with a harness and suspenders outfitted with Chi-Com ammunition pouches. Shoved down the top of the ruck was a sawed-off Ithaca 12-gauge shotgun. Another rifle barrel and gunstock protruded.

His mouth was still cottony from the Biere "33" Export he'd drunk the night before at the Morning Star bar. The debriefing at the Embassy Annex yesterday left him thirsty.

—There was a plot afoot in the country directed by the spooks who'd been running this country for years using the Special Forces as their private protection if shit went downhill in a plot.

Now the steam-bath of Saigon humidity left him feeling unwashed. He heard odd bells and engines; Lambrettas, Vespas, Dauphines. He thought of the year he'd spent on an A Team in Dak Pek, six miles from the Laotian border and isolated in the rugged Annamite Mountains; a year training Montagnard tribesmen in the art of war.

—Little Dien Bien Phu they called it so quiet, so violent, so green, if the North Vietnamese didn't kill you a tiger would it would be cold there today.

He spat toward a garbage-strewn gutter. He searched the left map pocket of his fatigues and removed a wrinkled package of Lucky Strikes. He rummaged through his right pant pocket and withdrew a damp book of matches. It advertised, "One- sixteenth of an inch from eternity."

A book of matches can be the most important thing in your pocket. In a few seconds the head of a match can tell you whether your tires may soon be rolling on borrowed time. Insert the head of the match into the middle grooves of your tires. If you can see half of the head, it's time to replace them with

nylon cord tires, the strongest tire cord going thanks to CHEMSTRAND @NYLON.

He removed and struck a match. It dissolved in wet sulfur on the striking strip. He tried two more. They disintegrated. He sniffed at the matchbook. *Biere "33" Export.* He added the matchbook to the gutter. Overhead was the marquee of the Majestic Theater.

—*This hotel my hero Audie Murphy stayed at while they were shooting that movie he was quiet american Diem Diem and CIA sponsored and protected that film I saw in Fayetteville and here is Majestic Hotel Continental Hotel Lam Son square all here but roles reversed today somebody was assassinated in that one we grew up playing my hero Audie Murphy in our little war games in the foothills everyone wanted to be Audie Jesus just look at his decorations more medals on his chest in two years than most got in 30 years now they mean something to me precious ribbons and he ended up staying in this hotel shooting his .45 or whatever blend he carried at lizards on the ceiling my hero have to read that book suppose to reveal the secrets of why we're here.*

He looked at the Marquee.

—Playing The Quiet American no something L'Ami de La Famille whatever that is.

A ship's horn sounded in a clear wail from somewhere on the *Ben Nghe* Canal. Yesterday he'd seen the smokestack of a container ship at buoy on the canal.

—Leaving town all points west Singapore, Bombay, Barcelona, Bremerhaven get out while the getting is good.

Young girls on bicycles wheeled by with *ao-dais* fluttering white petals in the wind. Airmen and soldiers loaded and unloaded from vespas, cyclos, and lambrettas that idled on *Tu Do* Street while drivers, impatient for the next fare, cajoled endlessly. The China Air Lines office was advertising cheap fares every Tuesday and Saturday roundtrip to Taipei, Super Constellation.

—Get out while the getting good.

—He walked past the opera house on *Lam Son* Square and the Continental Palace Hotel. Faded posters of Paris scenes covered the hotel's walls; a hydraulic lift in a wrought-iron cage sat dark and empty, its door half-open. He noted the terrace bar was caged by wire. *Protection from the errant grenade.* Bougainvillea climbed the wire. The terrace bar was crowded with drinkers. It wouldn't be in a few hours. He glanced at his left wrist.

—1013 hours hair of the dog.

He stopped briefly in front of Our Lady of Saigon cathedral and looked up at the statue of the Virgin Mary planted in the churchyard. She appeared to be holding the orb of the world in her cradling hands. The polished, granite pedestal upon which she stood was chiseled with an inscription:

REGINA PACIS
ORO PRO NOBIS

He thought Mary resembled a kaffiyeh-wearing Arab; a referee holding a basketball at center jump. A boy carrying an armful of newspapers came from the step-way beneath the Saigon Post Office clock and extended a copy toward him. He reached into his pocket, sorted fifteen piasters from a wad of folded bills and purchased a copy of the SAIGON DAILY NEWS from the young Vietnamese who was dressed in a loud cotton and silk au baba. He perused quickly the headlines below the ubiquitous

JAMES S. LEE & CO.,
Custom Tailors, Hand Tailored
In Hong, Okinawa, Japan, Korea

A phrase came to him.

—Nuestra Senora de la leche y bien parto our lady of bountiful milk and easy delivery. Spanish language about a Jewess posing in front of a French church in Saigon. Typical that send me to language school for a year to learn Spanish for Panama send me to Vietnam.

A bulletin kiosk was emblazoned with the announcement: *SATURDAY. ALL SOULS 'DAY. The* hours of mass listed below. *The day of the dead*, he thought. He felt, in a sudden breeze from the west, perfumes from Ben Thanh Market glutted with its noodles, fishes and fruits. He overheard a man in khaki standing next to a pedicab call out to a taxi driver.

"Thu Duc."

Thu Duc. He had just been in *Thu Duc.*

Special Forces Detachment A-413. Vined with macadam turns round tropical gardens and golden monks streets of light, gardens of semi-finest green scuttling about in emerald canopies, teal-skinned lizards, a capuchin monkey. The Imperial Tomb, historic and erect, preserved at the rate of VN$ 510 by provisions of Arrete No. 5—BKTDT/VP/ND. Gross vined bastions of Thuy van Street, Thu Duc National Orphanage hidden in bauxite and isorel construction . . . . Thu Duc Re-education Center, painted with Sodo Sand Phanrang for fireproofing with veneer of coconut fiber board, beds, now prostitutes of Dai-The-Gioi, Nag Bay, Hoa Huy, Khanh-Hoi, Can-ong-Lanh, Xam-an, Chi-Lang. Sleeping in gauze vestments with parched legs closed against the heat and flies.

He smelled rain in the air. A priest exited from the side of the cathedral carrying an unopened umbrella. He spotted a striking girl. Squatting, she chewed before a charcoal brazier. She held the half-consumed umbra of an egg containing the congealed and dark remains of a duck.

—They love those unhatched ducks delicacy boil them, eat them putrid breath it gives them she has a nice ass taut in black silk like to fuck that without the duck what time is the rain today?

Pulling the *DAILY NEWS* from his ruck, he saw the date. Friday, November 1, 1963. He scanned the lower right-hand corner of the front page. WEATHER.

Yesterday's temperatures:
(Fahrenheit)

	High	Low
Saigon	92.3	76.5
Dalat	—	—
Nha Trang	90.1	76.5
Hue	94.1	82.0

- Full moon
- Saigon area, Southern provinces and Central
- Highlands: Cloudy with scattered rains and thunder-
- showers mainly in the afternoon.

A Fiat 850 squealed by. License plate TN3G80.

—One-sixteenth of an inch from eternity?

He felt for his matchbook. Gone. he wondered. An old Vietnamese gentleman stood fingering paper and tobacco from a package of Burley & Bright Tobacco. A brightly colored menu in the window of Cafe DALA_. The letter T was dark and blended into a corkscrew shadow. DALAT?

1. *Bisque du Homard Omard–Omart?*
2. *Gigot de Moutons*
3. *Pommes de Terre Soufflees*
4. *Soufflees Rothschild*
5. *Friandises Fr–frrrrrrrr*
6. *Petits Fours*
7. *Fruits*
8. *Wines*

There were false pepper trees on the verandah and a huge Pepsi logo.

**PEPSI-COLA COLD
BEATS ANY COLA COLD!**

A cream and flame-orange truck of Foremost Dairies with the big, little **f**, *laitcon* something or other, passed by. He breathed deeply of the busy intersection at Nguyen Du Street and Pasteur redolent of rosewood, durian fruit, custard apples, diesel, and gasoline.

—I need to piss.

He crossed to the opposite curb and entered the one-step elevation of Givral's bar. He did an airborne shuffle to the bar; as he inched the right foot forward the left foot trailed. He elbowed his way through milling soldiers and civilians to the long mahogany bar and ordered a cognac. The crowded bar seemed to swivel toward him but step back at the same time.

"Martell, please."

He broke from the crowd into the bathroom at the rear. He grinned as he brushed aside the curtained entrance to the cement urinals. There was a strong stench of ammonia. Unzipped, he stood on foot pads molded around a floor hole below and guided a steady-yellow stream of warm piss into the dark French underground of Saigon. He stared blankly at the ceiling overhead then read with glazed eyes an inscription written in red ink on a sand-grey wall.

High above Cayuga's waters,
there's an awful smell,
Where ten thousand sons of bitches call
themselves Cornell.

—Probably from Brown they're the fancy shits running around here wearing the wash and wear what's the color of shit Brown Brown Brown.

He returned to the bar and paid for the glass of cognac.

"Coke, s'il vous plait," he asked the bartender, a pretty, young Vietnamese woman with her hair twined in a tight bun. He scanned the patrons and guessed that most of them were journalists. He could hear the hum of gossip about the rumored political conspiracy brewing for the last few days. Diem, Diem, Diems. She put the coke in front of him. He held out his glass for another cognac. Nobody there knew what he knew, he reckoned, or they wouldn't be there, or like him, they were just passing through.

Once more on the street, he could see the Gia Long Palace through a park planted with towering tamarind trees bearing black, bean-like pods of fruit.

—The Gia Long Palace the plot thickened.

He glanced back at the cathedral and to the adjacent Saigon Post Office with its five-foot clock built into the doorway arch. BUU DIÊN over the clock with the dates •1886•1891• inscribed below. 1021 hours. He looked at the large Rolex on his sweaty left wrist. 1031 hours. He noticed, for the first time, the face of a smaller clock between the two towers of the cathedral; just below a Latin Cross which more resembled a bat-winged gargoyle.

—The hands indicated 0400, or 1600 hours nothing synchronized about Vietnamese watches.

III.

As he walked by the palace and approached the neighborhood of high-priced villas housing Vietnamese aristocrats and American government officials he saw well-heeled Americans in shirt sleeves exiting off Pasteur Street and walking to someplace with determination. Foreign correspondents called this section of the city spook row; the subsidized homes of spymasters posing as government and charity executives. Tall, graceful elms and Saigon cassia lined Le Qui Don Street. The spice of the cassia scented the air round the villa-lined streets with a perfume that shielded it from the pedestrian odors that hung over the city.

—They made little effort to conceal their identities they often posed as diplomats, no doubt like Mrs. Smiths's husband probably the only one who didn't know what was going on was her.

The soldier walked slowly and studied the white and yellow stucco and terra cotta of the manor homes built years ago for wealthy French and Vietnamese; pastel villas hidden by cement and iron-rail walls splashed with flowering mimosa, bougainvillea, and barbed wire. A closer inspection revealed, at the top of eight-foot cement walls, broken glass stuck in mortar. The walls were splattered with dark, green-black mildew fed by the rains and heat.

As he came to the corner of Le Qui Don and Phan Than Gian Street, he was surprised to find that his destination was the largest and most elaborate of the villas he had passed. Strange, he thought. Twelve of his compatriots from A-413 were assigned to the villa of another official, a big American spook with a French name.

At the villa entrance, was a tall iron-grate fence. The villa was a three-story mansion painted in pastel cream and white with terra cotta roof and gables. A circular cement guardhouse with gun ports was anchored at the villa gate. It was manned by a Vietnamese soldier with a pitiful M-1 carbine at sling arms. It was rusty and probably had enough mold to make penicillin. The guard stepped from the guardhouse and rendered a sloppy salute to Sands. He pulled at one of the double swinging gates and allowed the soldier to pass.

—This is my back-up shit where's Audie when he is really needed my first line of defense?

A garage to the rear of the villa had been converted from a pagoda erected five-hundred years before the villa. The tail-end of a sky-blue and white 1961, two-door hardtop Ford Fairlane 500 XL, stuck out. Mature jacaranda trees planted on the front lawn dwarfed the main entrance marked by a staircase that climbed left and right to a portico covered by a balcony. Jalousies were painted the same pastel cream as the house. Decorative moldings and archways were painted in white. Chinese planters the size of drainage urns were filled with Japanese pines and areca palms. They were scattered on the stairwell and round the foundation of the villa.

Mother-in-Law's-Tongue was interspersed with luxuriant orchids about the grounds. There was a distinct scent of the frangipani blossoms that smothered the fragile Saigon cassia. A gardener tended the orchids while another rode a motorized tricar outfitted with a loading bin full of loam between its front wheels.

IV.

He climbed the left stairwell and knocked on the entrance door. A Vietnamese houseman, bowing, opened the door.

—This is security rat bag ARVN and house guys almost like an afterthought detail guess the bossman isn't worried.

"Coming," a deep voice from behind the houseman.

He waited, taking in the bright hallway lined with enormous glassed-in cabinets and white and blue vases aligned like steps; the tallest over seven feet.

"Yes," said Mrs. Smith, who stood nearly as tall as Sands. A large woman, she walked toward him with the coordination and grace of a runway model. She was wearing a soft float of silk jersey ornamented with a mixture of daffodil yellow, green, and lavender. The flowering silk gown appeared as solid as the stone kimono of Our Lady of Saigon.

"Yes, Captain." She addressed him by the rank on his beret. "Come in." She dismissed the houseman standing at attention. He bowed slightly and disappeared. "I know you're here to provide some security supervision because of the situation."

"Yes. I need to take a look around the grounds, especially the dormer windows fronting Le Qui Don Street."

Mrs. Smith beckoned him to follow her through the hallway to a large winding staircase contained in an atrium of light. A pleasant perfume trailed her. He recognized the scent, but the brand eluded him. Paris.

"All of the second and third floor apartments are up the stairway. Can I bring you something to drink? Tea or water?" she asked, studying the image of the strong, rough-looking man whose head, now bereft of the green beret, was crew-cut. His jaw was covered by a three-day stubble and his piercing green eyes reviewed her slowly. She noticed the thin scar stretching from his right nostril to his right hairline.

"Does anyone else live here?"

"No. No one. The staff live in the attached utility building."

"If you don't mind, I'll drop some of this gear by that window over there." He dropped his gear by the large, latticed window overlooking the front lawn.

"Yes. Fine. Fine." She saw he didn't enjoy idle chatter. "Please let me know what you need Captain." She turned and walked from the room and called the houseman.

A telephone big enough to beat a man to death sat on a shiny end table with finely carved legs. Next to it was a copy of the Saigon MAAG telephone directory; a gild-framed photo of a much slimmer Mrs. Smith, another woman and two men. Like a revelation. The short man on the left was none than Audie Murphy. The photo was taken in front of the Majestic Hotel. The man on the right was one of the two officials at the Embassy Annex directing the team assignments on this day of plotting.

—These people had been here since the making of the movie then.

He picked up the directory and casually leafed through the forty-odd pages. Listings for MAAG, the Embassy, USIS, USOM, churches, hotels, schools, garages, air, and the Government of Vietnam.

Palais De L'Independance, Dai Lo Thong Nhut.. 21584,21585

—The Gia Long Palace. He wondered if Diem and Nhus were home today.

He looked at the listing for Newspapers, Magazines & Press Correspondents. The American correspondent who'd followed him around at Dak Pet? What was the news organization?

Agence France Presse 21748

11 Truong minh Giang Associated Press 25536

158 d/3 Pasteur & 64 Ho xuan Houng Business International,Newsweek 25460

227 Ngo Dinh Khoi Figaro 23555

Associated Press .... 158D Pasteur, Apt 6

The Associated Press, 158 Pasteur. He looked out the window.

—Only a stone's throw from here.

He placed his ranger pack on the red and tan mosaic of a Persian rug covering the room's floor. He pulled from the pack the parts of a disassembled sniper rifle with matched ammo, a telescopic sight, the Ithaca shotgun, two boxes of 00 buckshot rounds, two boxes of flechette rounds, a K-Bar knife, two claymores, six frag grenades, six concussion grenades, a box of five morphine syrettes, a pill pack of amphetamines, two carabiners, and ten magazines of 7.62 ball ammo in addition to the twenty-five of 9 mm parabellum ammo he carried in the Chi-Com ammunition pouches. Last, he felt for his favorite weapon; a Mark 22 hushpuppy, 9 mm pistol with silencer. His jacket easily concealed it.

He assembled the M-14 rifle and fitted the telescopic sight to the scope mount on the receiver. He wouldn't have to zero the weapon on the first man over the ramparts, he thought. Just point and shoot. He aimed the rifle out the window. He leveled the barrel at the gardener riding the tractor. He squeezed the trigger. The firing pin clicked. He heard a muffled sound and turned. It was Mrs. Smith. She stood watching as he lowered the rifle to the floor. He studied her as he retrieved the shotgun and loaded it with flechette rounds.

She cradled, like a baby, a tall glass of tea topped with a slice of lemon. "I thought you would like something to refresh," she said, offering him the glass.

He replaced the shotgun on the floor and stepped over his equipment toward her. He took the tea from her.

"Thank you."

"Are you really going to have to use any of this?" she gestured toward the armaments stacked strategically around the room.

He saw that the weaponry and an intense soldier walking around the palace made her curious and perhaps, fearful. He drank the tea in quick swallows. He finished and handed back the glass.

"I take it that's your husband in the photo with you and Audie Murphy?"

"Why, yes it is. They were making the film, *The Quiet American*. We met many of the actors then. I befriended Giorgia Moll, the Italian actress who played the role of the Vietnamese Phoung in the film."

"So, you met Audie Murphy then?"

"I think the only time we saw him was for that photo opportunity. He was a very private person as I recall and also had his appendix removed somewhere out of country in the middle of making the movie."

He studied the picture finding it hard to believe that Audie Murphy had walked down the street a block or so from the Annex he had just left. "That is interesting." He said to her. "What's the name of the street on the backside of your property?"

—Tu Xoung Street.

"And Pasteur Street? Only a couple of blocks over from here, isn't it?" He pointed leftward out the window.

"It's behind the Abraham Lincoln Library. You can see it from here." She pointed at a solid grey building half-hidden among elms and tamarinds about a block away.

He picked a PRC-25 radio from the bottom of his pack and pocketed two frag grenades. He walked toward the staircase, made his way to the roof and looked at his watch. An eerie quiet descended upon the hurly-burley of Saigon. The city shut down from about 1200 until 1400 hours. It was naptime. The traffic slowed to a trickle, the hum of commerce lowered to a whisper. Just as he began to relax, even sink into reverie, he felt a deafening explosion and knew it came from the direction of Gia Long Palace. His watch now said 1330 hours, sharp. A staccato of automatic gunfire echoed from the walls. Police sirens wailed. At 1335 hours, a convoy of armored personnel carriers followed by Vietnamese soldiers running passed on Phan Thanh Gian Street toward the presidential palace.

The soldier went up to the attic lofts and opened the windows of a room facing on Phan Than Gian Street. He saw smoke unfurling over the towers of Our Lady cathedral. He would find out later that the Presidential guard barracks near the palace had taken a direct hit from an artillery shell. The gunfire and movement of troops seemed to be contained in the park or on the lawn of the palace complex. He removed the telescope from his rifle and peered like a ship's captain at the areas beyond Le Qui Don Street. The roof bars of the Caravelle and Rex Hotels were packed with crowds of gawking civilians and advisory personnel who lined the railings. They waved glasses and bottles, oblivious to the events that punctuated the excitement. Troops with light weapons swarmed over the red tile roofs of buildings near the palace.

Later, he moved intermittently between the walled grounds of the villa and the loft windows. He had radio contact with the Embassy. He listened to reports that announced Vietnamese Army units had attacked the Presidential palace. He watched Sky Raiders swooping down over Lam Son Square. At 1620 hours he heard cannon fire from an M-48 tank then an RPG explode. A fireball erupted near Pasteur Street and the Gia Long Palace.

As he passed Mrs. Smith during his round-robin reconnaissance he nodded.

"What is happening?" she demanded.

"An attack has been made on the Presidential palace."

She nodded, no doubt having heard it already on the radio playing below in the dining room.

He cocked his ear and listened to the static of the bulky Kalmar stereo radio tuned to Armed Forces Radio Station. The broadcast was coming from the roof of the Rex Hotel. He strained to hear a melody drifting from down the staircase like incense.

"Sounds like the Inkspots," he said to the air.

Don't you get a little lonely,
All by yourself
Out on that limb
Without himmmmmmm?

He continued to slink around the grounds of the villa. After darkness the street lights blinked three times then dimly illumined the grounds of the villa. A light rain fell between 1900 and 2000 hours. Gunfire and explosions grew closer then faded. He stood on the portico steps in the dark and listened to the rain patter on the terra cotta and fan-like leaves. As he drew deeply on a Lucky Strike, he heard Mrs. Smith call to him from the doorway.

"Captain. Would you like to eat?" she asked.

He pinched off the lit end and field-stripped his cigarette then placed the wadded paper in a pant pocket. He emptied his canteen and returned the cap. He was hungry.

"Yes, thank you."

"The staff left earlier. There are leftovers in the dining room." He could see the outline of her face but no features.

He followed her to the dining room. She closed the curtained French doors and turned on a small lamp. The table was teak and big enough for a Viking hall. It contained several platters and bowls covered with linens.

"Help yourself. Ms. Smith removed the linen from a platter. "This is prawn in coconut batter and fried." She uncovered a small bowl next to it. "This is a sweet and sour sauce for dipping." Yet another bowl was filled with crabmeat salad and avocado.

"Would you care for something to drink?"

"A glass of red wine" he said. Something heavy to wash down the feast, he thought.

"We don't have alcohol in the house." A Coca Cola?

"Tea will be fine." He answered.

A voice emanated from the radio:

You're tuned to the 820 AM spot, the 99.9 FM spot. This is AFRS Radio in Saigon. The time is 2135 hours. The American ambassador and the Commander, Military Assistance Command, announce that a curfew from 2000 hours tonight to 0700 hours tomorrow morning is in effect for the Saigon, Cholon, and Gia Dinh area. For their own safety, Americans should stay off the streets unless movement is absolutely necessary for the conduct of official business.

"What's going on Captain?" Mrs. Smith asked.

"I've heard that President Diem and his brother, Nhu, are no longer in the palace. It's rumored they're hiding in a church somewhere in the city," the Captain said.

V.

She smiled. "I am relieved they are seeking safety in the Lord."

The soldier gave Mrs. Smith a quizzical look. He wondered how she meant the remark.

Sensing this, she said, "They're Catholic, I know. Even so, they can find salvation in our Lord, Jesus Christ."

"What do you mean?" asked the soldier. "Catholics aren't Christians?" He dipped the coconut shrimp in the yellowish sweet and sour sauce.

"To gain entry into the Kingdom we must be born again in the blood of the lamb. Christ died on a cross for our sins. We must ask His forgiveness or be barred from eternal life."

"Don't Catholics ask forgiveness from priests?"

"Christ is the Son of Man. He submitted to terrible tortures at the hands of the Jews, Romans, and Catholics, and was crucified. He was willing to forego His divinity and drink from the cup of human suffering."

"The Romans were Catholics?" An original twist. Roman Catholics. "But," he interrupted, "Christ was a Jew."

"Of course, He was a Jew," she said, twisting a strand of her hair into a knot with her thumb and index finger.

"What do you mean?"

"You said that your Christ suffered terrible torture at the hands of the Jews. My impression was that you don't see Christ as Jewish," he said. He had picked up the crabmeat salad foregoing the avocado lumps and, using his index and middle finger, scooped large globs to his mouth.

Mrs. Smith stared, then frowned. "Captain, I don't need to be told who Christ was. Christ's suffering was so great, God, His Father, could not look upon His face as He hung on the cross at Golgotha. The heavens turned black with his anger.

The soldier looked out through a jalousied window at the darkness. Heat-lightning illumined a silhouette of dark clouds. A cusp of the full moon was just beginning to peek. The soldier licked his fingers then wiped his hand on his pant leg.

"I'm don't understand," he said.

"What don't you understand?"

"You think that the crucifixion was the worse suffering endured by a man on this earth?"

"Yes. Without his sacrifice and suffering there would be no spiritual redemption for mankind. Our Christ died for you and for me. He died that whosoever believeth in Him shall not perish, but have life everlasting."

The soldier, hearing an explosion in the distance, turned off the lamp and walked to the window. He searched the lighted lawns and fence. The guardhouse was still occupied. The streets were quiet.

"Well," he murmured.

"What. What is it?" Mrs. Smith sounded alarmed.

He ignored her concern. "You believe that man has never experienced suffering quite like your Jesus Christ's?" he thought of the small flask of cognac left in his pack.

"Yes," she said.

"Well, Ma'am. If you have a moment. A friend of mine. His name was Billy. He died about five months ago. He was north of here, on the Laotian border. He was captured by North Vietnamese Army troops. When we found him, he was dead. But, before he died, he was tortured. They mutilated him. He was shot, stabbed and blown up."

Mrs. Smith put her hands over her mouth.

"And the insects joined in while he was still alive, by special invitation. We found him tied to a tree. Something sweet and sticky covered him. They say that if your Jesus hadn't had company at the cross, wolves, coyotes, and whatever animals roamed the holy world, would have eaten his feet off."

—Mrs. Smith waved her hands at him. "Stop. Terrible things happen in war, Captain, but the death of your friend cannot compare with Christ's. I won't allow that comparison. I am sorry."

"But that's not my point Ma'am. The resurrection."

"I don't want to hear it," she said, her voice rising.

"Resurrection is the difference between Billy and Christ."

"What do you mean?" she asked, her voice taking on a tremor.

"As you said, your Christ was divine. He was God, or the son of God. He knew the plan. Die on the cross like a hundred thousand other dumb Roman victims did. Then resurrection, right? He knew when, where and how. Isn't that right?"

"What in earth are you getting at?" she barely suppressed a squeal.

"Well, Ma'am, what kind of sacrifice is there when you know you can rise from the dead in three days?"

Mrs. Smith raised her hands to her ears.

"Here's the truth. Ask my good buddy Billy, if he were around to ask, but he isn't. Never mind. Take me. I'm talking about me personally, Ma'am, and shoot me, gut me, splay me, run me through a meat grinder. Put the grinder setting on fine, and double grind me. It won't bother me. Won't bother me one bit, if you promise, NO! Guarantee me that I can come back from the dead in three days. Come back in one piece. Reassembled. You know what I mean? The same piece I was in when I left. I'll take that ride and throw in the salvation of the entire human race as a bonus."

Mrs. Smith had lowered her hands from her ears and wrapped herself with her large arms, as if against a chill wind.

"What I'm saying is this," the soldier said, now oblivious to Mrs. Smith's protestations. "There ain't any sacrifice in a crucifixion when you are promised resurrection tomorrow. There is no fear. There is no shame. There is no humiliation. Probably why Christ died so quickly. He said, Let's get this thing over with so I can get myself resurrected. And where's the sacrifice if you are immortal to begin with? Ask my friend Billy. He mulled this last over. Yes, ask Billy."

Mrs. Smith had said nothing. She was tapping her left foot. He could hear it smacking like gunfire in the distance. Her face had reddened. She advanced a step toward him and threw out an imposing right hand at him.

She screamed at the top of her voice,

"GET THEE BEHIND ME SATAN! GET THEE BEHIND ME SATAN!"

The soldier stepped to the table one more time. He kept his gaze continuously on Mrs. Smith and picked up a handful of the pan-fried coconut shrimp and secreted them in a jacket pocket. The dipping sauce was making for a deep thirst.

Mrs. Smith, lowering her voice to a shout, said, "Pack your belongings and get out. There will be no evil in this house." She pointed toward Le Qui Don Street. "**GET OUT!**"

The soldier stood in the light of the guardhouse and adjusted his equipment. He smiled as he retrieved his flask of Martell, opened it and took a long drink. He packed the Swedish Model 45. He cradled the shotgun in his left arm. He smoothly and expertly reached for his pistol wedged between his belt and the small of his back. He removed the Captain's bars from his beret and replaced them with the metal crest of arrows crossed upon a sword. He checked his Rolex. It was 2230 hours. It was still early in the insurrection. Perhaps he should join President Diem and brother Nhu and pray for mercy

THE ROMAN

Όμηρος περισσότερο από οποιονδήποτε δίδαξε ποιητές ο σωστός τρόπος να ψεύδονται.'

("Homer, more than anyone, taught poets the right way to lie.")

– Aristotle, **Περὶ ποιητικῆς** (The Poetics) 335 BC

How was this Roman manuscript written in CE 31 as an official report of the trial and crucifixion of Jesus Christ sent by Pontius Pilate to Tiberius Caesar Divi Augusti filius Augustus and circulated during the principate of Maximin Daia in CE 311—known to have existed, but also known to have been destroyed—-discovered?

The history of this discovery was a circuitous and serendipitous one and began with the Roman scribe and senator *Publius Cornelius Tacitus'* history, *Germania,* written in CE 98, and only rediscovered in 1425.

All copies of *Germania* were lost during the Middle Ages and the work was forgotten until a single manuscript was found in Hersfeld Abbey in present-day Bad Hersfeld, Germany. The manuscript contained several works of *Tacitus* to include *Germania*, and was named *Codex Hersfeldensis*.[30] The *Codex* was then brought to Italy, where Enea Silvio Piccolomini, later Pope Pius II, first examined and analyzed the book. This sparked interest among German humanists, including Conrad Celtes, Johannes Aventinus, and Ulrich von Hutten, and, ultimately, German national socialism (*Nationalsozialismus*). In 1902 a Professor Cesare Annibaldi discovered, in the library of Count Guglielmi-Balleani at Jesi, a *Codex* (*Codex Aesinas Latinus 8*) containing Dictys Cretensis' *Bellum Troianum* and Tacitus' *Agricola (folia* 52–65) and *Germania (folia* 66–75). On September 23, 1943 Heinrich Himmler, the head of the SS, on the orders of Adolph Hitler, headed up a 30 man SS detachment 80 miles northeast of Rome to go to Jesi on the Adriatic

---

[30] The *Codex Hersfeldensis* contained Tacitus' *De Origine* (*De Situ et Origine Germanorum*), etc. (12 *folia)*, *De Oratoribus* etc. (12 *folia), Agricola* (14 *folia),* and *Dialogus de Oratoribus* (18 *folia),* and Suetonius' *De Grammaticis.*

coast, and just south of Ancona, the regional capital, and find at Count Guglielmi-Balleani's Villa, *Fontedamo*, the *Codex Hersfeldensis* for the Nazi reliquary. But the *Codex* had been moved secretly, and Himmler and his troops found nothing to return to Hitler. The *Codex Aesinas Latinus 8,* possibly the same as that discovered at Hersfeld, and found by Professor Annibaldi in 1902, had been transported to the *Biblioteca Nazionale Centrali* in Rome (*Viale Castro Pretorio*, 105, 00185 Roma RM, Italy) where it remained undisturbed until 1994, when a graduate student of Johannes Gutenberg University in Mainz, Gottfried Leichenberg, rediscovered it. Leichenberg was researching the story of Hitler and Himmler's pursuit of the *Codex Hersfeldensis* (and, specifically, *Germania*) in his research at the *Biblioteca Nazionale Centrali*, and discovered the manuscripts now referred to here.

What is the "Provenance" of the discovered document?

In the *Aesinas Latinus 8*, unopened, and unread for almost two millennia, were three books of Tacitus' *Annals*. The *Annals* was a history of the Roman Empire from the reign of *Tiberius Caesar Divi Augusti filius Augustus* to that of *Nero Claudius Caesar Augustus Germanicus*, the years CE 14-68, and totaled 16 books, of which books 7-10 and parts of books 5, 6, 11 and 16 were destroyed. Published between CE 115-120, *Annals* survived only in the remaining volumes until Leichenberg's discovery. The three books previously counted among those destroyed, and never referred to in secondary sources from after the date of the *Annals'* publication, but now located in the *Aesinas Latinus* 8 were an intact Book 5, Book 6 and the heretofore missing Book 7. But it is the whole manuscript of Book 5 that provides a full account of the document long rumored as the CE 31 official report of the trial and crucifixion of Jesus Christ sent by Pontius Pilate to Tiberius Caesar. Book V, about the reign of Tiberius Caesar between CE 29-37 only survived in part. "In part," describes a total of four pages. The discovered whole Book V is composed of 120 pages, numbered from Part I to Part LXIX (Part 1 to 69; Book IV, intact, was 133 pages; Book VI, also a remnant, was 98 pages)[31] and contained within these found pages is a tale never heard in the history of Jesus Christ, his life and his death. It is the earliest history, pagan or christian, in which any remark concerning the event of the existence of a Jesus of Nazareth, or a Pontius Pilate, appeared and it is by a writer who was born within 25 years of the events described.[32]

---

[31] From the conclusion of Book V, which ends in CE 29, "*V. Igitur Caesar repetitis adversum nepotem et norm probs increpitaque per edictum plebe, questus apud patres quod fraude unius senatoris imperatoria* . . . ." to the opening of Book VI, which picks up in Part 6 in CE 31, ". . . *Quattuor et quadraginta orations super ea re habitae, ex quis ob metum paucae, plures adsuetudine* . . . ." is added the discovered 116 pages covering CE 29-31.

[32] Before this discovery of the whole Book V, the first appearance of a Roman reference to Jesus Christ and Pontius Pilate appeared in Book XV of the *Annals* covering the period CE 64 (The Burning of Rome). It seemed odd to appear in an AD 64 reference since Pontius Pilate, the fifth Roman prefect of Judea, held this office between AD 26 and 36, and he sentenced Jesus of Nazareth to death in CE 30 (as is given in Book V). The earliest, and therefore most historically unprejudiced record of this event was written by Tacitus (CE 56-120) somewhere near CE 116. This previously famous first reference was given in the

Where did Publius Cornelius Tacitus, CE 56-120, obtain the information he shared in Book V of the Annals?

As he did in all the Books of the *Annals*, Tacitus took the history of each year recorded in *Annals* from the Acts of the Senate (*Acta Senatus*, or *Commentarii Senatus*). The *Acta* were minutes of the discussions and decisions of the Roman Senate. Before the first consulship of Julius Caesar (BCE 59), minutes of the proceedings of the Senate were written and occasionally published, but unofficially; Caesar, desiring to tear away the veil of mystery which gave an unreal importance to the Senate's deliberations, ordered them to be recorded and issued authoritatively in the *Acta Diurna*. Tacitus, as a writer and Senator, had access to the commentary and used them in full. From the recorded sessions

---

Annals, Book XV, Chapter 44: *Auctor nominees jus Christus, Tiberio imperitante per Procuratorem Pontium Pilatum supplicio affectus est.* . . . ("Christus, from whom the name had its origin, suffered the extreme penalty during the reign of Tiberius at the hands of one of our procurators, Pontius Pilatus . . . ."). The missing 116 pages of Book V, now explain these remarks on the history of the Republic in Book XV, some 34 years later.

of CE 30, which once composed only four pages of the *Annals*, the 116 pages offering the entire disclosures of that year and of the trial of Jesus Christ are now related, in part, here.

Does the evidence revealed in Book V of the Annals come from Jesus Christ's appearance before Pontius Pilate in April of CE 30?

No. In the canonical gospels, Pilate's court refers to the trial of Jesus Christ in *praetorium* before Pontius Pilate, having been preceded by a Sanhedrin trial. In the Gospel of Luke, after the trial by the Sanhedrin, Pilate finds that Jesus, being from Galilee, belonged to Herod Antipas' jurisdiction, and so decides to send him to Herod. The rest of the canonical history records Herod's inspection of Christ to be short (Jesus did not answer) and observing that Jesus posed no threat, returned him to Pilate for trial. But in Book V, the events of Jesus' appearance before the Sanhedrin, all recorded by Sanhedrin functionaries, were provided *sua sponte* because of the Roman court's denial of jurisdiction. The findings of Pontius Pilate were, therefore, based on *inventiones a legalis* by the High Priest and the Sanhedrin. The recorded testimony of Jesus before the Sanhedrin began on the Thursday night with an informal inquiry based on various accusations: violating the Sabbath law (by healing on the Sabbath), threatening to destroy the Jewish Temple, sorcery, exorcising people by the power of demons and claiming to be both the Messiah and the Son of God. The informal inquiry, followed by an official trial Friday morning was conducted at the house of *Joseph Ben Caiaphas* the High Priest of Israel, where the functionaries (scribes and the elders) were gathered. Built on the side of Mount Zion, it was recorded that this split-level house had three tiers, including a courtyard, a slaughter room and a dungeon. Jesus was held captive overnight in the dungeon after the official preliminary inquisition by Caiaphas and the Sanhedrin.[33]

[33] Here, in the discovered Book V, Part XXVII (Book 5, Part 27) of the *Annals*, begins the segment of recorded testimony included in the official report of the trial and crucifixion of Jesus Christ, *inventiones a legalis* sent by Pontius Pilate to *Tiberius Caesar Divi Augusti filius Augustus* and still extant in CE 311 when it was rumored circulated during the principate of *Maximin Daia*. All of the proceeding text follows from Part 27.

Where did the interrogation take place?

The official report to Tiberius Caesar revealed that after using the guards to beat and mock Christ, Caiaphas had planned an interrogation that went on from mid-evening Thursday through half the night of Friday morning. Caiaphas had Christ led to the close, gloomy, vaulted prison in the ancient palace of the Holy and shut him in it. Afterward, in the pitch darkness the iron door of the dungeon was suddenly opened and Caiaphas himself, with three guards, came in with a candle in his hand. Caiaphas was not dressed in his ornate High Priest robes as he had been in the afternoon, but instead wore a coarse monk's cassock and a striped scarf wrapped around his head.

How did the interrogation proceed?

Caiaphas approached Christ and gazed into his face. He went up slowly, set the candle on the table and motioned to the three guards to stand next to Christ at the ready. He began his questioning thus. "They say you have a mother, Mary? There is no mention of you having a father? Who is your father?" Christ did not answer. Caiaphas motioned to a guard who reached out and struck Christ in the face. A second guard took his arm in a levered lock and began to exert breaking pressure. Christ answered, "One who knows his father and mother will be called the son of a whore." Caiaphas answered him, "Your least fear here is being the son of a whore. Who is your father?" Christ looked down and answered, "*Tiberius Julius Abdes Pantera*." Caiaphas, knowing this already, said, "You went to see your father when you reached your 18th birthday? You were gone 13 years from this land? Where did you venture?" And Jesus answered "*Mogontiacum.*" And Caiaphas asked, "Where is *Mogontiacum*?" And Jesus answered "*Germania*."

Who was Tiberias Julius Abdes Pantera and how had this relationship with Jesus Christ arisen?

Tiberius Julius Abdes Pantera came from Sidon, and at age 22 (BCE 3), joined the *Cohors I Sagittariorum* (first cohort of archers).[34] At the

---

[34] The names *Tiberius Julius* were acquired later in recognition of his serving in the Roman army as he gained Roman citizenship: Tiberius because he

time of Jesus' birth in Nazereth, Pantera was with the *Cohors I* in operations suppressing a revolt at Sepphoris near Nazareth. It was taught in the *Talmud* that Rabbi Eliezer said to the Wise, "Did not *Jeshua ben Pantera* (Jesus Christ) bring spells from Egypt in a cut in his flesh?" and they said to him, "He was a fool, and they do not bring evidence from a fool. *Jeshua Ben Pantera* is son of *Ben Pantera*." Rabbi Hisda said, "The husband was actually *Pappos ben Judah* (Joseph), the lover was *Abdes Pantera*, the mother was Miriam (Mary) the dresser of women's hair. As we say in *Pumbeditha,* 'She has been false to *Satath da,* her husband.'" And *Jeshu*a was also known as *Jeshua ben Stada*, the son of Stada, but this name was given to Miriam as an epithet which derived from the Hebrew/Aramaic root "*sat ah/sete* (to deviate from the right path, to go astray, to be unfaithful)." Miriam was also called "*Stada*," because she was a *sotah,* a woman suspected, or

---

served under the Emperor Tiberius. The name *Pantera* is Greek. In Greek it means "panther." His first name, "*Abdes*," means "servant of God" (Latin form of Aramaic *Ebed*). and would indicate that Pantera had a Semitic, or even Jewish forerunner. *Kélsos* (Κέλσος), Λόγος Ἀληθής, (*Logos Alēthēs);* the discovered fragment).

convicted, of adultery.[35] One year after Sepphoris and the birth of Jesus, Pantera was dispatched to the *Legio XIV Gemina*, a Roman heavy infantry regiment with archers, in *Mogontiacum*, one of eight legions commanded by *Lucius Domitius Ahenobarbus* after Pantera's arrival. Later, Pantera would fight in a battle victory against Germans under *Germanicus Julius Caesar*, which triumph was honored by his adopted father, the Emperor *Tiberius Caesar.* After that battle the Regiment was distinguished by the cognomen *Martia Victrix* (martial and victorious).

When did Pantera arrive at Mogontiacum and when did he depart?

Pantera served in the Roman stronghold or *Castrum Mogontiacum,* the precursor to Mainz, from his arrival in BC 1 until his death in CE 37. *Mogontiacum* was founded by the Roman general *Nero Claudius Drusus Germanicus,* perhaps as

---

[35] The *Tosefta*, the *Qohelet Rabbah* and the *Jerusalem Talmud* (Hebrew: תַּלְמוּד יְרוּשַׁלְמִי, *Talmud Yerushalmi*, often *Yerushalmi* for short) make explicit connection with Yeshu *(Yeshu ben Pantera)* as the "son of Pandera"; cf. *Toledot Yeshu*, (ספר תולדות ישו).

early as BCE 13/12. Although the city is situated opposite the mouth of the Main, the name of Mainz is not from Main, the similarity being perhaps due to diachronic analogy. Main is from Latin *Menus*, the name the Romans used for the river. Linguistic analysis of the many forms that the name "Mainz" has taken on make it clear that it is a simplification of *Mogontiacum*. The name appears to be Celtic, but it had also become Roman and was selected by them with a special significance. The Roman soldiers defending *Gallia* had adopted the Gallic god *Mogons* (*Mogounus, Moguns, Mogonino*), for the meaning of which etymology offers two basic options: "the great one", similar to Latin *magnus*, which was used in sycophantic naming such as *Alexander magnus*, "Alexander the Great" and *Pompeius magnus*, "Pompey the great", or the god of "might" personified as it appears in young servitors of any type whether of noble or ignoble birth, but it is not shown to be the case in *Mogontiacum*.

Why was Mogontiacum important to the Roman Empire?

Mogontiacum was a strategic military town throughout Roman times, probably due to its unique position at the confluence of the *Main* and the *Rhenus* (Rhine). The town of *Mogontiacum* grew up between the fort and the river. The *castrum* was the base of Legio XIV Gemina, and SVI Gallica (CE 9–43), XXII Primigenia, IV Macedonica, (CE 43–70), I Adiutrix (CE 70–88), XXI Rapax (CE 70–89), and XIV Gemina (CE 70–92). It was also a base of the Roman Rhenus fleet, the *Classis Germanica*. The city was the provincial capital of *Germania Superior*, and had an important funeral monument dedicated to *Drusus*, to which people made pilgrimages for an annual festival from as far away as Lyon.

Did Caiaphas receive an explanation from Jesus Christ of his voyage from Palestine to the far country of Germania and Mogontiacum?

And Caiaphas asked of Jesus, "How knew you to go to *Mogontiacum?* And Jesus divulged his visit to Sidon to find the family of the father who had been rumored to him for so long. His mother, Miriam, had released to him that the mother of *Tiberius Julius Abdes Pantera* was named *Mara* of

Zaraphat and that she last lived in Sidon.[36] With this information Jesus proceeded to Sidon. Caiaphas asked him, "Were you alone?" And Jesus answered that he was not but traveled with James, son of Alphaeus, his eldest brother who knew Sidon well, having been a grown man when Jesus was born in Nazareth to Miriam. And Caiaphas asked if he found his father. And he answered that he had not. But he had found Pantera's mother, *Mara*, just southeast of the port of Sidon at *Darb El Sim* near the banks of the *Sayniq* River. An old woman, her

---

[36] Jesus entered Sidon with James in approximately CE 16, at about the age of 18 years. This remarkable fact is confirmed by the biblical, talmudic and mythical references that record that this son of Sidon, reentered the city in CE 29 for some mysterious and never explained reason. Mark in the earliest gospel says that Jesus Christ visited Tyre and Sidon a year before his death, or about CE 29: "And from there he arose, and went away into the borders of Tyre and Sidon. And he entered into a house, and *would have no man know it*; and he could not be hid" (Mark 7:24). When Jesus returned, he went through Sidon back to the Sea of Galilee, not the most direct route and no one can explain this. Mark 7:31. [διὰ Σιδῶνος] (see the critical remarks): We may however, perhaps, trace the feeling which prompted the visit in the words of John, that there was an interest in "Other sheep, not of this fold,"; John 10:16.

memory failing, she could only recall that Pantera was a soldier of the Legionary 14th of *Gemina* and had journeyed to a place called *Germania*.

What did Jesus do with this knowledge, vague to him, but exact in its identifying information?

James led Jesus to the quays of Sidon where he knew the Roman Navy was replete in fleets of transport ships leaving continuously with the materials of military support to the far-flung *Imperium populi Romani*. And in their questioning and explanation of his young brother's search to both soldiers and sailors at the dock, they discovered his military father was in *Mogontiacum, Germania Superior* (the name 14th Legion of *Gemina* provided the answer). It was given to them that a large Roman grain ship was leaving on the eve to cross *Mare Nostrum* to a final port at *Aquileia* at the northern tip of *Mare Supĕrum*. The passage for this 18-year-old son of a Roman Legionnaire to *Aquileia* was figured at 50 denarius (200 sesterces). The ship, named *Gaulus*, a 100-ton cargo vessel carrying 10,000 *modii* of grain, had a crew of five and was a single master outfitted with a large square sail.

By what course did Jesus plot his maiden seafare to Mongontiacum on the grain ship Gaulus?

Through the gates of the north port of *Sidon* westward to *Rhodes*, 36.2433° N, 27.9718° E, southwestward toward *Creta*, 35.2401° N, 24.8093° E, a mild westward leg past the ancient lands of *Macedonia* with its *Sparta*, 37.0745° N, 22.4303° E, and *Olympia,* 37.6385° N, 21.6299° E perched on far hills; again a westward odyssey past the island of *Ithaca*, 38.4285° N, 20.6765° E, to the port of *Corfu*, 39.6243° N, 19.9217° E, and a first mooring at *Brundisium*, 40.6327° N, 17.9418° E, where many tons of *Gaulus*' cargo were unladen. After this, a course was set due northwest to *Salona* 43°32′22″N 16°28′59″E and final arrival in *Aquileia*, 45.7682° N, 13.3687° E, where the crew and accompanying passengers deported. Jesus then traveled with soldiers, amongst whom he counted an archer, farmers, an architect, a musician carrying a lituus, a physician, two engineers, two teachers, a writer and poet, a smith, three entertainers, an artist and an attachment of slaves, transporters, and families, from *Aquileia* on the *Viae Romanae*

Maiores to *Cremona*, 45°08′N 10°02′E, *Augusta Praetoria*, 45°44′N 7°19′E, *Augusta Raurica*, 47°32′2″N 7°43′17″E, *Argentoratum*, 48.5827°N 7.751°E, and finally to *Mogonticum*, 50°0′N 8°16′E, on the *Rhenus*.

Did Jesus recount any significant memories of his first voyage upon the seas of Mare Nostrum and Mare Supĕrum?

Yes. Two. The first while sailing along the eastern coast of *Mare Supĕrum* after leaving *Brundisium*. As the sun rose near the shores of the ancient city of *Split*, a mist hung over the sea as the *Gaulus* rounded a scarp. As Jesus watched from the bow, he was amazed to see a man walking toward him on the misty waters a good distance from the shore. He exclaimed to a crew member and pointed. The sailor told him that it was an oyster fisherman working in the hanging frames of an oyster garden tending to oysters as in an olive grove but on a floating skiff and explained to him what an oyster was. As the mists lifted and the oyster man approached, Jesus saw him balancing broad legged in the flat boat with almost no silhouette. He could also see a building on pylons shoreward, and that many men in skiffs were affixing roped, hemp bags from hanging frames. The ship-hand called out to the water-walker and beckoned him alongside, asking for a sample of his oysters which were piled high on the skiff floor. The oyster man opened several quickly and passed each up to the sailor who shared them with Jesus saying to him, "Take Eat." When Jesus took it into his mouth, it was tender yet springy, bursting with sweetness and a finish that tasted like watercress and a certain melon he had once had in Nazareth. It amazed him entirely, as if it all been in a dream, or another world.

What was the second of these memories?

The second memory was of the dark night air of the deck beneath a starlit sky in the middle of *Mare Supĕrum.* He inquired of the same sailor who had given him instruction in oysters how the ship was guided in sail at night by the captain. His teacher told him that the helmsman was called *gubernator,* or *palinurus* and steered the ship with a knowledge of the sun, stars, and weather, all gained over 30 years of sailing *Mare Nostrum.* He told Jesus there were scores of stars that guided the hand of the *gubernator* by night and they were named by Greeks, Romans, Phoenicians, Egyptians and even by mysterious tribes above the northern lights;

Alpheratz, Ankara Schedar, Achernar, Hamal, Menkar, Mirfak, Rigel Bellatrix, Betelqeuse, Sirius, Pollux, Regulus, Menkent, Kochab, Antares, and Nunki, the constellation of the holy city, to name a few. And Jesus asked him if all sailors learned the stars and his pilot answered, "Yes. The importance of their sailing skills were to protect the transportation of oil, wine, fish products, spices, cloth, ore, marble and, stone blocks. Even wild animals arriving from Africa and elsewhere for use in the games.

Did Jesus find his father upon arrival in Mogontiacum?

When Jesus arrived, his father, Tiberius Pantera, was recovering in the *valetudinarium,* the large military hospital, from wounds he had received in a recent battle against a tribe of Germans called the *Marsi*. His wounds were slight but he had distinguished himself under the command of *Germanicus Julius Caesar.* The *Legio XIV Gemina*, came under ambush returning to *Germanicus*' winter quarters at Mogontiacum, but inflicted heavy losses on the enemy. These battles had been ongoing and in reprisal for the terrible losses the Roman armies had taken under

Publius Quinctilius Varus at the hands of the German commander, *Arminius*, in the Battle of Teutoburg Forest six years before.

How did Tiberius Pantera react to finding a young man claiming to be his son by Miriam of Sepphoris?

Tiberius Pantera was a professional soldier for as many years as Jesus had lived. He said nothing for a long while and stared at Jesus who had provided enough information that he knew this must be the child of his union with Miriam when he served with the *Cohors I Sagittariorum* during the Syrian rebellion at Sepphoris. Roman command was under the leadership there of the self-same *Publius Quinctilius Varus* who lost his head at Teutoburg Forest along with three legions of the Roman army. But he had left *Sepphoris* for *Mogontiacum* within a year of his encounters with Miriam and after she had disappeared. She was alleged to have been taken by her family, and now revealed to him for what purpose her disappearance: the concealment and birth of his son named *Jeshua Ben Pantera*. And he called from his bed to Jesus and welcomed him with open arms and said unto him, "So this is my beloved son? I am well pleased."

And how did this reunion transpire for father and son?

They spoke of many things over this period of reunion. Jesus told his father of the beauty of Nazareth where he grew up; of the plateau of Zebulun and Naphtah; the mountains of Lebanon with snow-covered Hermon towering above them all and to the west Tyre and the blue waters of *Mare Nostrum*; Mount Carmel, the Plain of *Esdrelon* and the green hills of Gilbon, Mount *Eral* close by; and, the Sea of Galilee, Gillead and Tabor where a landscape, extensive and beautiful spread as fine as any in the world. He remembered sitting on a hill near the Roman Road, "The Way to the Sea," connecting Damascus and Sidon; the caravan route to Jerusalem that he and his family traveled every year for the Feast of Passover to Jerusalem along the Plain of Jezreel; and the spring of Nazareth that gave them its replenishing waters. His childhood days brought immeasurable memories of meal, women grinding at the mill, sowing and reaping, the sparrow and the lily;

children in the market place, weddings and funerals. In reply to his father's questions about his education, he said that he read and spoke Aramaic, Hebrew and *Koine* Greek and had studied from his sixth year under *Chazzan* the *Pentateuch*, followed in his tenth year by the *Mishnah* and in his 15th by the *Gemaras*. And Pantera asked Jesus about Sepphoris. "Did you ever see it?" And Jesus recalled for him Sepphoris, the Capitol of Herod Antipas and the military stronghold in Galilee across its rolling hills. He remembered for him how his step-father, *Joseph Ben Jacob*, took work in the grand building projects of Herod as a stoneworker and carpenter and how he had apprenticed in these trades for the years before his journey to *Mogontiacum*.

Did father impart to son such like-kind information about himself?

Yes. He spoke of his history after leaving Sepphoris and Syria. The construction of causeways called *pontes longi* on the bogs of the Rhine under the command of *Lucius Domitius Ahenobarbus* when he arrived in *Germania* as a young soldier. In the next years, the conflicts between the Rome and the *Cherusci*. His service in the command of *Marcus Vinicius* over the five legions stationed in *Germania*. And then under Tiberius who was appointed by Augustus Caesar to the Rhine frontier as the commander in *Germania* and the adventures against the *Canninefati*, the *Attuarii*, the *Bructeri* and the *Cherusci*; in battle with the Roman fleet and legions on the Elbe; and, building a winter base at Lippe. And how his luck had saved him from the massacre at Teutoburg Forest because the Commander, *Publius Quinctilius Varus* had camped on the Weser taking three legions (*Legio XVII*, *Legio XVII* and *Legio XIX)* six cohorts of auxiliary troops (non-citizens or allied troops) and three squadrons of cavalry, sending the *Legio XIV* back to *Mogontiacum* under the command of his nephew *Lucius Nonius Asprenas*. Tiberius Pantera told his son that at Teutoburg Forest some 20,000 Roman legionaries and auxiliaries died surrounded by German tribes led by their commander, *Arminius*. And this included captured Roman soldiers and auxiliaries crucified by *Arminius* along the exit roads from Teutoburg Forest. He recounted the next decade of campaigns led by Tiberius and his son-in-law, *Germanicus Julius Caesar*, in which a further 20,000 Roman troops were killed during the self-same foreign warfare. And Jesus saw that his father was very moved in the retelling of these accounts and sought to comfort him.

Caiaphas asked Jesus about his education in Mogontiacum and how he had come to Latin and Greek, which he knew Jesus spoke fluently and read?

From the poet and writer who had traveled with him to *Mogontiacum* when he was still a young man. *Lucius Cornelius Sulla Felix*, had begun his tutelage almost immediately, Jesus having, as he had as a boy in the temple, a voracious appetite for learning. In the villages of Nazareth and Capernaum in Galilee, where Jesus spent his boyhood, he spoke Aramaic, had learned Hebrew from his trips to the temple and knew enough *Koine* Greek to converse with those who were not native to Palestine. In the next ten years of his education, he became fluent in Latin and Greek, reading *Terence, Horace, Virgil, Livy, Plautus, Sophocles, Cicero, Persius, Ovid, Strabo, Aristotle, Plato, Catullus, Caesar, Varro, Nepos, Lucretius, Sallust, Cato, Aristophanes, Herodotus, Sophocles, Euripides, Plutarch, Ennius,* but foremost, *Homer*. He expressed he took great interest in *Homer*, and the tale of *Odysseus* who also was a carpenter, with his suffering life and his attempts to return to his fatherland where he hoped he would be welcomed. But, even more so, because the the first four books start with the son of *Odysseus, Telemachus'* journeys in search of news about his father, who had not returned home from the Trojan War. And most coincidently, *Telemachus* translated from the Greek to "far from the battle," or perhaps, "fighting from afar," as a bowman does, thereby taking Jesus and his father into account in one fell swoop. Like *Odysseus*, Jesus wondered if, upon his return, he would be doubted, asked the wrong questions, shown ignorance. He wondered would he have to go in disguise like *Odysseus* to regain his house, live a long and prosperous life, or would death be his lot? For some reason, the tale of *Nausicaa* had appealed to him. It was the story of *Odysseus* making entry into a city in anonymity with the assistance of *Nausicaa*, a beautiful princess of the *Phaeacians,* with a resemblance to the goddess *Artemis. Nausicaa*, using her guile, finds him mules to ride into the city late in the day, carrying laundry, with branches and fronds cut from the fields. Jesus found wonder too in *Odysseus*' awe at seeing fig trees in the garden of *Alcinous* which bore fruit all of the year round. And the description of *Ithaca*, the very island he had passed asea to port in *Brundisium*, stayed with him still, as he recited it to Caiaphus in his perfect Greek.

εἴμ᾽ Ὀδυσεὺς Λαερτιάδης, ὃς πᾶσι δόλοισιν
ἀνθρώποισι μέλω, καί μευ κλέος οὐρανὸν ἵκει.
ναιετάω δ᾽ Ἰθάκην ἐυδείελον: ἐν δ᾽ ὄρος αὐτῇ
Νήριτον εἰνοσίφυλλον, ἀριπρεπές: ἀμφὶ δὲ νῆσοι
πολλαὶ ναιετάουσι μάλα σχεδὸν ἀλλήλῃσι,
Δουλίχιόν τε Σάμη τε καὶ ὑλήεσσα Ζάκυνθος.
αὐτὴ δὲ χθαμαλὴ πανυπερτάτη εἰν ἁλὶ κεῖται
πρὸς ζόφον, αἱ δέ τ᾽ ἄνευθε πρὸς ἠῶ τ᾽ ἠέλιόν τε,[37]

Caiaphas asked if Jesus worked as a carpenter in Mogontiacum, as had been his other father's occupation when he worked in Sepphoris?

And Jesus answered him that *Joseph Ben Yacob's* work was as a *tekton,* and that he worked as a builder of buildings and had taught Jesus

[37] I am Odysseus, Laertes' son, world-famed For stratagems: my name has reached the heavens. Bright Ithaca is my home: it has a mountain, Leaf-quivering Neriton, far visible. Around are many islands, close to each other, Dulichion and Samos and wooded Zacynthos. Ithaca itself lies low, furthest to sea towards dusk; the rest, apart, face dawn and sun.

carpentry to help in all of these constructions. After his father had arranged his housing in the *Castrum praetorium* that included Pantera's move from his own barracks, he brought him to the master carpenter's workshop near the *principia* situated by *Drusus' Cenotaph.* Jesus became a master carpenter under the tutelage of *Titus Nonus Faustus* and remained so until his departure from *Mogontiacum.* He believed that this would be his work in Judea for he had no hopes of extending his family bonds to another task as his father had explained that as any child born during their fathers' military service was deemed illegitimate, regardless of whether these fathers were Roman citizens and whether they served in legionary or auxiliary units and, therefore, in consequence, such children had no claims to their father's estate.

Did Jesus have a special memory of his work in Mogontiacum?

In the list of his craftsmanship, Titus Faustus sometimes fashioned crosses used by Roman command after a tribunal order to carry out sentences of execution. Titus Faustus had pointed at the treed hillside across the Rhine near the *Castellum Mattiacorum*, saying to Jesus, "That is where the crucifixions take place as well as the woods from which the oak, and pine and plane trees grow to make the crosses." The first confession Titus Faustus made to Jesus was a story of crucifixion by the Cherusci of Roman soldiers after Teutoburg Forest; how living soldiers were covered with wild beasts' skins and torn to death by dogs; or they were impaled, or hung, *crucibus adfixi* was the term he used; and, when daylight failed, the dead and dying were burned to serve as lamps by night to deliver more. This shocked Jesus greatly but he would read soon the intimation of these deeds centuries earlier in Homer's *Iliad* and *Odyssey* under the tutelage of Lucius Felix. Such events as πήξαι ἀνα σκολόπεσσι, where glorious Hector bids someone to cut heads from tender necks and fix them upon poles. He knew that in Homer's texts σκόλοψ usually referred to stakes, probably pointed. But now crucifixion was quite a different practice, a thing, he realized in shaping and making his first crosses in the workshop of Titus Faustus. Homer seemed to describe this crucifixion in the *Odyssey*, for a suspension crucifixion was mentioned by him regarding the punishment of the suitors in the twenty-second book of the *Odyssey* with instructions to bend and tie the feet and hands of Melanthius above him and to tie boards behind him and having tied a twisted rope from him, drew him high to the roof beams that he, being alive for a long time, suffered grievously. And now a whole vocabulary for nailing; *clavus, figo, affigo/ adfigo, offigo, suffigo, antefigo, and καθηλόω/ προσηλόω*; for tying *spartum, alligo,* sometimes *προσδέω,* and *κρεμάννυμι.* In this shop, Jesus, with disgust and fascination, assisted Titus Faustus in preparing the *crux immissa (crux sublimes), stipes cruces,* and the *patibulum* of his first cross, and many more over the next decade. The weight of a cross, 300 to 800 pounds, sometimes astounded him; the patibulum, the bar portion of the cross the victim was forced to carry could weigh 30 to 80 pounds. The Romans had perfected this purposeful and scientifically devised ritual to produce maximal agony and prolonged suffering, and bloodless, the victim sometimes enduring four to six days before death fell.

Did Jesus ever take a woman during his work and education at Mogontiacum?

No. Like Mithras, Jesus had remained celibate all of his life. But he remembered a dancing woman of one of the tribes of Germania in the canteen at the praetorian for soldiers who used to dance on a threadbare carpet by the light of a smoky lamp, waving her arms as she clanged small wristlet cymbals. Her loins arched, her head low to the ground, and, seemingly dragged down by the weight of her heavy, fiery hair, her eyes brimming with voluptuousness, eager, languishing, compliant, she would have made Artemis herself grow pale with envy. "I was in love with her barbaric dances, her voice raucous yet sweet, the atmosphere of incense, the semi-somnambulant state in which she seemed to exist. I had followed her for a while, among the rabble of soldiers, conjurers, extortioners, and lotharios, who surrounded her, but she disappeared and I saw her no more. I was reminded of her by a woman who came to me from Magdala, near the Sea of Galilee. She danced and had the same red-flashing hair. For some reason, upon meeting her, she washed my feet with her long tresses. If I were to tell the truth, if I had not matured so long ago a taste for wine in Germania, I may have fell to these temptations of the flesh."

How did Jesus take leave of Mogontiacum and his father before his journey back to Judea, Samaria and Galilee?

Before the date of Jesus' departure by land caravan with the *Cohors SVI Gallica*, which was returning to *Roma* by way of *Ravenna*, Tiberius Pantera, returned from a campaign in *Baduhenna* Wood where the *Frisii* had crucified Roman soldiers to collect taxes and forced the governor to flee to a Roman fortress which they then besieged. *Lucius Apronius*, *propraetor* of Lower *Germania* called upon the Legions of *Moguntiacum*, auxiliary infantry and cavalry, to throw the *Frisii* out. Tiberius Pantera had returned to *Mogontiacum castrum* from there, worn and tested, but uninjured and eager to make his son's departure a memorable one. To this end he prepared an *Agape* Feast for Jesus in the manner of a *Mithraic* gathering, inviting familiars of the 14th, some of the friends of Jesus and a preparation staff of ten mess stewards taken from the *castrum* kitchen which fed over 4000 men. Along the steep hillsides of the Rhine, grape cultivation amongst the wild *vinifera* vines begun with *Drusus*, had been advantaged. The hillsides of *Mogontiacum* offered the added benefit of shielding vines from the cold northern winds, and the rivers' reflection offered additional warmth to aid in ripening the grapes and now the product was imbibed by the soldiers of *Germania*'s Legionnaires. And Jesus had witnessed for his ten years in that place the Romans diluting the strong wines stored in ceramic ware containers and sometimes in rock cisterns with voluminous pours of water. They explained to him, when he asked the first time, that the wine had heavy evaporation and became stronger while aging, hence watering, and it had struck him that to drink the undiluted wine would have been like partaking of poison. But he had come to a great affection for the watered wine of Romans and had often thought that the pouring of the waters of the Rhine into the large containers gave the illusion of turning water into wine. And there was the Roman brew *cerevisia* which Tiberius Pantera preferred to wine, as did most of his compatriot legionnaires. And as the *Agape* Feast of Jesus unfolded, Tiberius Pantera provided a familiar menu of the foods that Jesus had eaten in Nazareth; unleavened bread, olive oil, honey, lemon figs, olives, parsley, lamb, pomegranate juice, apples, walnuts, all included in dishes of cholent, olive hyssop, charoset, haroset and salads of bitter herbs and lettuce, and staples of the Roman tongue; celery, taro, flower bulbs, cabbage and other brassicas, courgettes, cardoons, and leeks. And a small succulent clam that recalled to Jesus the oysters he had first tasted at *Split*, and poultry, roasted, braised and boiled. A braised pig took a place of honor and a sausage made from its meat and entrails. And snails, and dormice (considered a delicacy in Rome among the wealthy) and quinces, currants, damson plums, rose hips and more exotic zeroes and medlars. And *moretum* for spreading on bread, a standard ration for Roman soldiers. G*arum*, *liquamen*, *muria*, and *allec* sauces, and to favor the Roman soldiers, diluted with wine, which had in itself been diluted with the Rhine, to go with the fishes appearing at the table; a sturgeon and its roe, river and brook lamprey, white bream and houting.

And what was the setting of this Agape Feast for the man Jesus and his farewell?

It occurred after a deep snow fall, in *Menses*. Jesus had experienced cold and snowier times in his intervening years in *Mogontiacum* and he could always mark his birthday with the snows of the winter solstice on the Rhine. It was a time when the river was frozen and crowds walked upon the waters of the Rhine as if it was a highway for oxcarts instead of boats. He had even seen a skiff rigged with a cloth skimming over the ice like a racing chariot. And this in turn triggered a memory in the heat of summer when early-morning mists were rising from the great Rhine as Jesus made his way from the Jupiter column towards the quay near *Dimesser Olt*. He saw a soldier walking atop the river toward the *Castle Mattiacorum*. Walking on the water. Not on a bridge, but standing atop the mist that covered the river's surface, as if elevated. It seemed to him that this was defying the Greek laws.[38] He had run

[38] Any object, totally or partially immersed in a fluid, is buoyed up by a force equal to the weight of the fluid displaced by the object. The upthrust (of a body in a given medium) is equal to the difference between the weight of the solid and the fluid displace. V=K (W-M).

towards the quay to keep this apparition in his view and saw that the soldier was on the other side of the Rhine. Some peripatetic Legionary, or mercenary in the regent force of Tiberius Claudius Nero Caesar, Conqueror of the Elbe and the Rhine, who had lost both legs in Teutoborg Forest to the *Cherusci.* But he would be much older, not spry like this apparition. Two wooden legs carved by someone like Titus Faustus, the cross-maker, or himself, from applewood, or pine; floating over the Rhine like a water glider. A magician; sorcery, γοητεία; a deceiver for that is what magic is. Piling green -stained stones from the river's edge in strategic submarines from the weathered quay toward the eastward shore of the *Castellum Mattiacorum*. And it was all the more memorable for the feast of food and drink that warmed all the gathered and the view of the *Castellum Mattiacorum* seen through a mist across this, now, river of ice from the house of celebration near the column of Jupiter. And for the honor by a father to his son for a life well-lived in this place so strange and far from his home, for lo, these past years. It was this setting and farewell that he would carry with him to *Judea*.

Caiaphus finally asked Jesus how the religion of his childhood had failed him.

Caiaphus said unto Jesus, "We believe in one God, we believe in the covenant which God had made with his people Israel, and we believe in the foundational book of this covenant, the Law of *Adonai*, the *Torah*. You returned from *Germania* with other covenants." After reflection, Jesus answered him, "The Romans of my father and of the fathers of *Germania* worshipped many Gods. *Mogontiacum* was said to have been named after the Celtic god, *Mogons*, but I saw no evidence that this worship was present during my years. The Legionnaires of *Mogontiacum* were worshippers of *Mithras*. My father was a follower because *Mithras*, born of a rock in the winter solstice, was a soldier, invincible and eternal in battle, the slayer of demons promising strength and success to his followers in this world, but most rewarding, a special afterlife in another world." And he said also, "*Mithras* was born of *Anahita,* an immaculate, virgin mother once worshipped as a fertility goddess and subsequently given the title 'Mother of God' and incarnated into the human form of the 'Saviour.' *Anahita* was believed to have conceived *Mithras* from the seed of

Zarathustra preserved in the waters of Lake *Hamun,* and thus *Mithras* remained celibate throughout his life and ascended to heaven 64 years after his birth. He raised the dead and will find them at the end of time. He relegated the wicked to a hell and will establish a millennial kingdom one day upon this land." Caiaphas asked him, "Who followed this *Mithras* then?" Jesus said, "In *Mogontiacum*? Followers were soldiers, imperial and all ranks, officials of the civil service, traders, craftsmen and the lowborn and slaves of the *castrum*. Groups of worshippers gathered loyally and held fealty to each, as to their god." Caiaphus looked at Jesus and asked, "And were you a follower of this god?" And Jesus answered, "I have tried to live my life according to the example of *Mithras,* as well as others. But a disciple? I can not say that I am. I have opened a new path for the light of my father." Caiaphas asked, "Which father is that, and what light?" Jesus answered, "My father *Tiberius Caesar Abdes Pantera* and the light that guided him, *Mithras*. I wish that I could show you *Germania*, or Ithaca, or Greece, and stand in front of certain shrines and sacred streams and say, 'Look. Living is only comprehensible through a thousand local gods. Not just the old dead gods, with names like Zeus; but, living geniuses of place and person. Not just Greece, but modern Rome, here in Jerusalem. Here. In spirits of certain trees, of certain curves in a rock wall, of certain fish and oysters, of the packed dirt roads to Sidon, if you like, and fig trees that always bear fruit and frowns in people, slouches. I'd say to them, 'Worship! All you can see. And more will appear.'"

Did Pontius Pilate write the "official" report of the trial of Jesus Christ to Tiberius Caesar Divi Augusti filius Augustus in CE 31?

No. The report, composed by Roman scribes at the court, was made from the interrogation transcription of Caiaphas, *inventiones a legalis*, certified by Herod Antipas and directed to *Tiberius Caesar* by courier after the conduct and crucifixion of Jesus Christ.

Was there ever a response by Tiberius Caesar to Pilate's report of the trial of Jesus Christ?

The *Commentarii Senatus* of the Annals show no mention of a response by Tiberius Caesar.

How, then, do we know the conclusions of the Republic regarding the trial of Iesus Nazarenus Rex Judaeorum?

From Tacitus' recording of Pilate's appearance before Caligula, in Rome, CE 37. We have been instructed by these facts. The discovered Book 7, counted among those books destroyed and never referred to in secondary sources after the date of the *Annals'* publication, but now located in the rediscovered *Aesinas Latinus 8*, recorded the missing trial documenting Pilate before *Gaius Julius Caesar Augustus Germanicus* (Caligula), CE 37. Book 6 of the *Annals* had ended on the death of Tiberius Caesar in CE 37 (Book 6, Chapter 51; Tiberius Caesar died in *Misenum* on 16 March AD 37, in his seventy-eighth year). Chapters 1-4 of the discovered *Annals,* Book 7, provide a record of what happened on Pilate's return to Rome to stand before Caligula, who succeeded Tiberius Caesar, his adoptive grandfather, as Emperor. Tiberius Caesar, had died even as Pilate was returning to Rome to appear before him to answer for the mass killing of Jews in a place called Mount *Gerizim*. Tacitus revealed that Pilate's removal as governor occurred after Pilate ordered the slaughter of a group of armed

Samaritans at a village called Tirathana near Mount *Gerizim*. It was alleged that they hoped to find artifacts that had been buried there by Moses because the ground was important to the Samaritan idea that Mount *Gerizim* was Israel's one true sanctuary; it was the only place where sacrifice, prayers and praise were acceptable and even after destruction of the Samaritan temple the beliefs associated with the mountain continued calling it the gateway to heaven. This incident occurred in CE 36, prior to the Day of Atonement celebrated in September, which allowed time for the delegation to *Lucius Vitellius* the Elder, the Roman governor of Syria, to argue its cause against Pilate and ended with *Vitellius'* recall of Pilate to Rome to be judged by Tiberius. The trial, as recorded in the *Acta Senatus*, revealed that Caligula asked Pilate to explain *Vitellius*' recall of him before Tiberius and now himself. Pilate testified to this. That a rebel leader of the Samaritans who made light of mendacity and in all his designs catered to the mob, rallied them, bidding them all to follow him to Mount *Gerizim*, which in their belief was the most sacred of mountains. He assured them that on their arrival he would show them the sacred vessels which were buried there where Moses had deposited them. His hearers appeared in arms and began climbing the mountain in a great multitude inviting into their ranks new arrivals as they climbed. But before they could ascend, Pilate blocked their march up the mountain with a detachment of cavalry and heavily armed infantry, who in an encounter with the first comers in the village slew some in a pitched battle and put the others to flight. Many prisoners were taken, of whom Pilate crucified the principal leaders and those who were most influential among the fugitives. *Vitellius* thereupon dispatched *Marcellus,* one of his friends, to take charge of the administration of *Judaea*, and ordered Pilate to return to Rome to give the emperor his account of the matters with which he was charged by the Samaritans. And so, Pilate, after having spent ten years in *Judaea*, returned to Rome in obedience to the orders of Tiberius Caesar, and since he could not refuse. And Caligula accepted all of this noting that Pilate had served the Republic in office for more than ten years, where good men only lasted twelve to thirty-six months at the most.

How did the discussion of the trial of Jesus Christ in Jerusalem conducted six years past, arise between Pilate and Gaius Caligula?

And Caligula said to Pilate, "It is now time for you to retire. But there is one thing I require to know. In reading the collection of the Mount Gezirim revolt, there was also an old report of a trial conducted by you as *Procuratori Judaea* of a certain *Iesus Ben Pantera*, or *Ben Stada*, namely *Iesus Nazarenus Rex Judaeorum*, who claimed to be King of the Jews and perform miracles, or perhaps more, sent by you to Tiberius several years ago. The rebel was crucified and the attention of him in your file came to me because I have heard other things since about this unfortunate son of a Roman soldier." And saying so, Caligula asked Pilate if he remembered this man and the incident. Pontius Pilate frowned, and his hand rose to his forehead to explain a deep contemplation that has found nothing. Then after a silence of some seconds: "Jesus?" he murmured, "Jesus—of Nazareth? The name is strange to me." And Pilate, answering as honestly as his memory would allow, said, in his own defense to Caligula, "During the ten years of my governance I judged hundreds of rebels, thieves, agitators, thaumaturges and insanities and crucified many of them, but the son of a Roman soldier? Reports of certain trials required by Tiberius Caesar were completed by the government's scribes, by the Jewish authorities, even by Herod Antipas, and forwarded. I am sorry Caesar, but I have no memory of this particular name, or why the son of a Roman soldier stood trial before me, let alone to be adjudged." Caligula said, "It is of no significance." He thanked Pilate for his voyage, his answers and inquired finally of him, "You have a Villa I am told, near Jupiter Vesuvius. Will you take up residence there?" And Pilate answered his Caesar that he would take recourse at the waters of Baiae with the Phlegraean plain stretching out to the ruins of Cumae, and pay homage to Tiberius Caesar each time he glanced out toward Cape Misenum where Tiberius had taken his last breath. Caligula said he knew well the name given from the helmsman of Odysseus' ship, and the graceful outline of that coast, its gardens, and its marble terraces along the shore and even more so, the Campanian coast, adorned in fireworks when the sun sank over gleaming temples which far away rose above the laurels of Pozzuoli and Vesuvius. With these thoughts, Gaius Caligula bade Pilate farewell.